Captive
Invertebrates

Captive Invertebrates

A Guide to Their Biology and Husbandry

Fredric L. Frye, B.Sc., D.V.M., M.Sc.
Fellow, Royal Society of Medicine

KRIEGER PUBLISHING COMPANY
MALABAR, FLORIDA
1992

Original Edition 1992

Printed and Published by
KRIEGER PUBLISHING COMPANY
KRIEGER DRIVE
MALABAR, FLORIDA 32950

Library of Congress Cataloging-in-Publication Data

Frye, Fredric L.
 Captive Invertebrates: a guide to their biology and husbandry
  p. cm.
 Includes bibliographical references and index.
 ISBN 0-89464-555-2 (acid-free paper)
  1. Invertebrates as laboratory animals.   2. Invertebrates as pets.
 3. Captive wild animals.   I. Title.
 SF407.I58F79   1991
 639'.4—dc20
                                                    90-25062
                                                      CIP
10 9 8 7 6 5 4 3 2

Contents

To my wife Brucye, who, although never professing a fondness for lowly creatures who spin webs, leave slime trails, or scurry about on six or eight legs, nevertheless has cheerfully shared our home with many of these beasties, and to Doctor Milton Hildebrand, professor emeritus, Department of Zoology, University of California, Davis, whose teaching skills and enormous enthusiasm in his lectures, laboratory, and on field trips were inspirational to a generation of biological science students.

Books by the Author:

HUSBANDRY, MEDICINE, AND SURGERY IN
CAPTIVE REPTILES

BIOMEDICAL AND SURGICAL ASPECTS OF
CAPTIVE REPTILE HUSBANDRY

PHYLLUS, PHALLUS, GENGHIS COHEN AND
OTHER CREATURES I HAVE KNOWN

FIRST AID FOR YOUR DOG

FIRST AID FOR YOUR CAT

SCHNAUZERS, A COMPLETE OWNER'S GUIDE

MUTTS, A COMPLETE OWNER'S GUIDE

BIOMEDICAL AND SURGICAL ASPECTS OF
CAPTIVE REPTILES, 2nd Ed.

A PRACTICAL GUIDE FOR FEEDING CAPTIVE
REPTILES

IGUANAS: A GUIDE TO THEIR CAPTIVE CARE

Acknowledgments

I am indebted to my editor, Edna Perkins, for her patience and insight in making this text as readable and "user-friendly" as possible. Ms. Perkins freely admitted during the early editing of the manuscript for this book that as a student, she had skipped biology entirely. As I read her comments penned in the margins of early drafts of this manuscript, it was obvious that she had done her homework, albeit a bit tardily.

I am most appreciative to Marie Bowles, Production Manager at Krieger Publishing. Marie's personal warmth, editorial craftsmanship, and enthusiasm for this project made it one of my most pleasant writing efforts.

Also, I am grateful to Doctor Charles Judson, professor of entomology, University of California, Davis, for his helpful comments on early drafts of this effort and for writing the Foreword.

Foreword

Dr. Frye has made another valuable contribution to our ability to better understand the "lowly creatures."

He has brought together, from many relatively obscure or unavailable sources, the information needed for successful husbandry of interesting and diverse representatives of several invertebrate groups. He has emphasized many seemingly unimportant facts, or those of which we are unaware, such as the need for suitable hiding/resting space, which can mean the difference between a satisfactory or an unsatisfactory effort. An awareness of such facts will contribute to the successful rearing of individual specimens or the establishment of colonies of these animals. Biology teachers, zoo or museum personnel, biological researchers, and the interested lay person will be better able to maintain healthy creatures when supported by the information presented in this book.

Reading this book will lead to greater understanding and appreciation of the intricacies of the biologies of these beasties and the roles they play in our environment . Our evolving awareness of the values of these animals to our understanding of Nature, and as research "tools" or subjects, emphasize the importance of their maintenance and husbandry.

Dr. Frye's timely work will make an important contribution to this end.

Charles L. Judson
Professor of Entomology
University of California at Davis

Introduction

In their book, *Fleas, Flukes and Cuckoos,* Miriam Rothschild and Theresa Clay commented, "Human beings are apt to regard their own personal structure as 'normal' and everything that differs from it as distinctly humorous. It is difficult for them to realize that fleas breathe through holes in their sides, have a nerve cord below their stomachs and a heart in their backs, or that certain other arthropods lay eggs through their elbows, urinate through their heads, and regularly practise virgin birth."*

Even as a very young child, I was fascinated by invertebrates, especially spiders and scorpions and the process of insect and amphibian metamorphosis. Although my father usually took a decidedly dim view of my collection of living creatures, I was fortunate in having a mother who, while not liking spiders and scorpions, at least accepted them in her home—as long as they were securely housed in escape-proof quarters. Many times she interceded with my father who, having reached a threshold of tolerance, was finally disuaded from banishing my menagerie to a museum or zoo. My mother also insisted that my captive charges were fed and cared for before I could expect to receive the same consideration from her. It was a remarkably wise and prescient policy that I have followed as a parent.

My youthful fascination with invertebrates is shared by more people than I realized.

An ever-increasing number of zoos and aquaria around the world exhibit collections of living insects,

*Rothschild, M., and Clay, T.: **FLEAS, FLUKES AND CUCKOOS.** Collins, London, England; 1952.

spiders, scorpions, crabs, snails, slugs, and other invertebrates. Such displays can be seen at the Smithsonian Institution's Museum of Natural History in Washington, D.C.; the Milwaukee Public Museum and Zoo; the Staten Island Zoo, New York; Steinhart Aquarium, San Francisco; the Living Desert Museum, Palm Desert, California; the Sonoran Desert Museum, Tucson, Arizona; the Insect House, Zoological Society of London in Regent's Park; and several institutions in Japan and Germany, to name but a few.

Some zoos are devoted entirely to invertebrates. In some, the center of interest is the production of particularly beautiful tropical moths and butterflies; others emphasize enormous stag, rhinoceros, and elephant beetles, or giant mantids, phasmatid stick and phylliitid leaf insects, and large spiders. Examples of such institutions are the Butterfly Houses at the London and Glascow Zoos; Stratford-on-Avon; Marine World-Africa USA in Vallejo, California; the Butterfly Park on Sentosa Island adjacent to Singapore; and the splendid Insect Zoo in Penang, Malaysia. These public exhibits feature screened greenhouse-like enclosures through which visitors may stroll and see magnificent flamboyantly colored insects amid lush tropical vegetation. Each exhibit has proven to be educational and highly popular with the public.

Wholesale animal dealers list an ever-widening variety of invertebrates in their sales brochures. Currently, the armchair traveler can order over a dozen different kinds of mygalomorph spiders, several species of exotic scorpions, huge centipedes and millipedes, and a few species of large praying mantis and stick insects. Huge "whistling," "hissing," and other sibilant forms of cockroaches are readily available to those whose interests run to the exotic.

The growing interest in invertebrates has a practical as well as aesthetic basis.

Some invertebrates are being studied in relation to comparative neurology, physiological chemistry and toxicology. Others are under investigation because they possess one or more special chemicals or properties that may prove useful for the betterment of human health. With the destruction of many rain forests, there is a sense of urgency to identify and study as many of these creatures as possible before habitat loss leads to extinction.

From ancient folk medicine to modern science, invertebrates have shown the way to life saving advances. A brief review of their uses should convince even skeptics of invertebrates' value to man.

Throughout the ages, enormous numbers of insects, arachnids, and their invertebrate kin have enthralled and, sometimes, served people. Since humans first began making their living as hunters and gatherers, honey has been used as an energy-rich foodstuff, and there is ample evidence that ancient medicine men and women knew of the healing properties of honey when it was applied even to infected wounds. Some ulcerated lesions today are treated with this old remedy. Between 1970 and 1990 several important papers were published in reputable medical and biochemical journals describing the antimicrobial properties of propolis or "bee glue." Grange and Davey (1990) reviewed the literature relating to this resinous substance and found that extracts of propolis exerted a significant inhibition of the growth of a variety of known pathogenic bacteria, including even the causative agent of human tuberculosis. There is evidence that propolis may inhibit tumor growth and even kill some cancer cells. Furthermore, this substance has been shown to enhance the generation of bone, cartilage, and dental pulp (Stojko *et al.* 1979; Scheller *et al.* 1977, 1978). Similarly, some spider, scorpion, and poisonous cone shell venoms are being studied for their effects on nerve conduction, chronic pain, and blood coagulation.

In ancient Egypt, Greece, Rome, China and India, various "lower" animals were regaled or reviled for their imagined powers to bring fortune or misfortune. The scorpion was elevated to a sign of the zodiac, and the common house cricket was, and still is, considered to be a good omen throughout much of China and Japan. The medicinal leech, *Hirudo medicinalis*, is still employed today in treating a variety of blood-related illnesses and postoperative complications, especially following plastic and reconstructive surgery. In 1984, Biopharm (UK) Ltd. established a farm in Swansea, Wales, to distribute leeches and their purified secretions for medicinal use and scientific investigation. Learned societies have been founded that are dedicated to the study and conservation of leeches and several international conferences devoted to the biomedical applications of the medicinal leech have been held—and well attended.

Other invertebrates are being employed in studies directly applicable to human health. For instance, bivalve mollusks such as clams, oysters, and mussels serve as "sentinel" animals for monitoring environmental pollution. These lower animals are exquisitely sensitive to environmental toxins including heavy metals, mutagens and carcinogens to which all animals, including humans, are vulnerable.

Invertebrates have also served as comparative models for biomedical study. The horseshoe crab, *Limulus polyphemus*, and the American lobster, *Homarus americana*, have been used for investigation of cardiovascular circulation; photoreception; mechanisms of blood respiratory pigments; blood coagulation; the role of specific cells in blood clotting; and osmoregulation (the balance between water and salts in maintaining fluid-electrolyte relationships). Marine corals, sponges, sea urchins, starfish, sea cucumbers, sea slugs, sea hares, and marine worms are being used to study immune responsiveness involving cell-mediated immunity. The role of hormones and hormone-like bioactive substances in regulating growth, regeneration of lost body parts, and reproduction has been investigated extensively in lower animals as diverse as segmented worms, mollusks, starfish, sea urchins, and crustaceans. Crabs have served as models for the study of the regulation of blood glucose, tissue fluids and their inorganic salts, heart rate, and the ability to change colors. The photoreceptive retinal pigments of some crustaceans have been used as models for the study of sight in higher animals, and the entire field of neurophysiology has benefitted substantially from the use of many sea creatures as subjects in nerve impulse conduction research. Many factors that govern longevity have been explored using a variety of invertebrates, especially insects such as the common fruit fly, *Drosophila melanogaster*. Cephalopods such as the octopus and several varieties of squid have been invaluable research subjects for numerous studies into comparative physiology.

Perhaps most exciting, invertebrates have been employed as models in cancer research and tissue transplantation studies. Even some of the most simple creatures have been found to develop spontaneous tumors. Leukemia-like disorders have been found in invertebrates, especially some insects. For tissue transplants, graft acceptance and rejection are being investigated with increasing multidisciplinary interest. Invertebrates lack a thymus, specific immunogenic cells, and other sophisticated antibody producing structures that are present in vertebrates. Therefore, these creatures are particularly valuable for the study of immune protective mechanisms that function in the absence of antibodies or "killer" leukocytes.

Besides providing models for medical research, the culture of invertebrates offers a way out of a distinctly modern dilemma. Because of their brief generational times, many insect species under intense selective pressure can take advantage of mutations that render their successive generations increasingly resistant to many chemical pesticides. Shortly after the chlorinated hydrocarbon DDT was introduced and used widely, it was found that DDT-resistant flies and mosquitoes were evolving rapidly. Meanwhile, the nonselective pesticides were exterminating many beneficial insects and arachnids. The use of natural predators instead of chemicals offers a solution to this problem. The best known example of integrated pest management is the release of the common ladybird beetle to control aphids.

Further uses of captive invertebrates are found in the commercial testing laboratory and classroom.

The "animal welfare movement" has sharpened awareness that higher animals may not be necessary—nor even desirable—for some areas of biomedical research or the teaching of biology. Today, invertebrates are taking their place in some of these activities.

With invertebrates being kept for so many uses in entertainment, research, agriculture, medicine, and education, a need has arisen for a practical guide for their care. This text was written to serve as a handbook for both professional and amateur collectors of those invertebrates that are kept as pets or subjects of biological study. These include "tarantulas" and other arachnids; scorpions; pseudoscorpions; whip scorpions; solifugids ("sun," "wind," and "camel" spiders); centipedes; millipedes; praying mantises; stick and leaf insects; aquatic insects; stag, rhinoceros, and elephant beetles; terrestrial, arboreal, and aquatic hermit crabs; crayfish; terrestrial and aquatic gastropods; and turbellarians.

The culture of invertebrates for food for higher life forms in captivity is also discussed. These invertebrates include crickets, meal beetle larvae, wax moth larvae, mulberry silk moth larvae, fruit fly and housefly larvae, and earthworms. Bees and beekeeping have been omitted purposely because these subjects have been covered adequately in other publications.

Many of these creatures are short lived under the very best of captive or wild conditions; some live for several decades, but these are the exceptions. Some general knowledge of the biology of these species is essential, and I have included references for further study to better understand these interesting animals.

The basic information necessary for the successful management of captive invertebrates in health and safety is furnished in this book. Where appropriate, consideration for safety measures for both the captives and their keeper is provided. As is true with many diseases of vertebrates, inadequate environment and diet often lead to failure in captive invertebrate husbandry.

Acquired diseases often owe their induction to inadequate husbandry procedures. Infectious and parasitic diseases, traumatic events, and toxic chemicals exact their toll, but careful attention to housing and nutrition is essential. Obviously, the *prevention* of husbandry-related problems is paramount because remedial action is often impractical.

The clinical signs of disease in invertebrates are often the same as those one would expect to observe in the higher life forms. These signs include lethargy or torpor; anorexia; the loss of the righting reflex; abnormal posture; external lesions involving the exoskeleton or cuticle; abdominal distention; or weight loss. In those animals possessing hairy exteriors, alopecia (baldness) may be observed. The cuticle may be discolored and/or periodic molting may be impaired.

Metamorphosis, an amazing process through which a primitive juvenile worm- or fish-like larval form of a creature undergoes transformation into an entirely different kind of animal, must be understood to appreciate fully the biology of insects. Metamorphosis occurs in animals as disparate as insects and amphibians. With respect to invertebrates, metamorphosis can be either complete or incomplete. Complete metamorphosis proceeds from egg to larva to pupa (or chrysalis) to sexually mature adult. Incomplete metamorphosis differs in the absence of a worm-like larval form, and goes from egg to nymph stages, to sexually mature adult. In this text, examples of complete and incomplete metamorphosis will be discussed and contrasted so that the reader will become familiar with this vital characteristic of many insects.

It seems natural for the public to approach the veterinary profession when seeking husbandry information in general, yet because of a lack of knowledge and interest in these creatures and the lack of sufficient economic incentive, veterinarians have often lost their role (by default) to others such as agricultural extension personnel and high school biology teachers. The pet trade has found many invertebrate creatures to be popular; the day may be dawning when veterinarians also will provide accurate and appropriate information and services related to these species. It is a minor detour from providing medical care to vertebrates to providing medical care to animals lower on the phylogenetic scale. Clinical diagnostic procedures are limited largely to visual observation, microbiological cultures and the microscopic examination of stained cytological specimens for pathogenic bacteria, fungi, and protozoa. For the present time, antibiotic therapy and the application of veterinary surgery will, most likely, remain limited to limb amputations and assistance in relieving difficulties during periodic molting.

Philosophically, I disdain keeping wild animals in cages; therefore, I would be among those who advise AGAINST keeping many of these animals in captivity,

Also, some of these creatures represent health hazards to their human captors. However, people *will* keep a wide variety of animals as "pets" or study models. Under these circumstances, the least that I can do as a health care professional is to assist in keeping these interesting beasties cared for properly.

Fredric L. Frye

1

Caging

ACCOMMODATIONS FOR
TERRESTRIAL INVERTEBRATES

Providing a safe, sanitary, and uncrowded environment for captive invertebrates usually is a simple matter of using discarded or easily modified containers such as wide-mouthed glass or plastic jars, screened cages, or aquaria. The capacity of the container depends upon the nature, size, and number of terrestrial invertebrates to be kept in confinement. Small trapdoor spiders, "tarantulas," scorpions, pseudoscorpions, whip scorpions, solifugid sun or wind "spiders," centipedes, millipedes, and terrestrial hermit crabs can be kept in one-gallon glass or plastic mayonnaise, mustard, or pickle jars. These discarded containers can be obtained at most restaurant or fast-food franchises. Large "bird-eating" spiders and "tarantulas" are best kept in aquaria with a capacity of at least three gallons (approximately 12 liters). Often, a leaky but intact aquarium can be obtained for a greatly reduced price from a pet store or aquarium hobbyist dealer.

The vast majority of invertebrates are kept at average room temperatures and do not require external heat sources. These animals will, however, exhibit stress and may die if they are exposed to elevated temperatures, especially if they are confined in closed glass containers that are placed in the sun. These glass jars or terraria absorb, accumulate, and retain external heat from radiant solar energy. Therefore, these containers must not be placed near a window or left outdoors in an unshaded area. If supplemental heat is necessary, it can be safely furnished by placing a heating pad or heating cables *outside and beneath* the jar or terrarium.

The litter or substrate provided for captive invertebrates depends upon the natural habits of each species. Clay cat litter type material should not be used because it is highly absorptive and may create an insufficiently humid environment for some species. This can lead to difficulties in the periodic shedding of the outer epidermal cuticle or exoskeleton. Some arachnids need a thick layer of cage litter; the fascinating and industrious trapdoor spiders construct tubular burrow-like nests lined with silken web material and covered with a closely fitting beveled and hinged lid that they hold closed from within. The "tarantulas" and other terrestrial mygalomorph spiders spin surface webs or sheet-webs and do require a deep layer of litter in which to burrow; they will, however, use a piece of curved oak or other hardwood bark as a refuge. Terrestrial hermit crabs thrive if coarse sand covers the bottom of their cage. Whatever material is used must be cleaned as soon as it becomes soiled with feces, uneaten food, insect parts, or shed exoskeletal debris. The entire substrate should be removed and replaced with clean material at least twice a year, or more often if necessary.

If living plants are to be part of the terrarium, some provision for lighting and drainage of excess water must be included in the plan. If dry branches or flat stones are used as cage "furniture" in the container, they must be adequately propped or anchored so that they cannot topple over and crush the inhabitants.

Some invertebrates will drink water from shallow vessels; others must have their water furnished as small dew-like droplets deposited on foliage with a misting device such as a hand-held spray bottle. An appropriate means for providing water to each of the creatures in this book will be mentioned briefly. It is vital that these animals' environments be furnished in a way that is compatible with the habits of each particular species.

Depending upon the nature of the cage, some provision for air circulation must be made. Spiders, scorpions, solifugids, centipedes, millipedes, and hermit crabs kept in wide-mouth jars can be prevented from escaping and still receive adequate ventilation from a few small holes drilled or punched in the metal jar lid. If these holes are punched with a nail or ice pick, they should be directed from the inside of the lid to the outside. This will provide a smooth inner surface, thus discouraging the inhabitants of the container from clinging to the underside of the lid and escaping when the lid is removed.

ACCOMMMODATIONS FOR ARBOREAL INVERTEBRATES

The large mygalomorph ''bird-eating'' spiders (''tarantulas''), orb-weaving spiders, praying mantises, stick and leaf insects, moths and butterflies are kept optimally in large upright cages or terraria furnished with appropriate foliage, branches, or other objects upon which to rest, feed, or spin their webs. Some circumstances permit the inclusion of living plants such as small succulents or cacti; in other cases, bare branches are more appropriate. Whatever elevated objects are placed in these cages must be firmly anchored to prevent them from becoming dislodged and injuring the inhabitants of the cage. If the cage has solid walls, a few small holes or cracks should be provided for air circulation, but they must be small enough to prevent escape.

Most arboreal invertebrates obtain their moisture from plant juices or from the body fluids of their prey. However, both vegetarians and carnivores will imbibe water droplets from foliage or web strands. It is imperative that the cage not be permitted to become too humid and fetid because these conditions will promote the growth of pathogenic bacteria and fungi that can be harmful to captive invertebrates.

ACCOMMMODATIONS FOR AQUATIC INVERTEBRATES

Aquatic spiders, water beetles, water striders, dragonfly nymphs, and other denizens of the pond can be kept conveniently in conventional aquaria furnished with water plants that are anchored firmly in the bottom sand or gravel. In some cases, a water filtration system must be provided, but this depends upon the capacity of the tank, the nature of the captive invertebrates, and their dietary habits.

The flourishing aquarium is provided with living algal plants, protozoa, and other lower multicellular plants and animals. Aquaria with natural plantings are not only more aesthetically pleasing but are partially self-supporting; when an adequate light source is available to permit photosynthesis, necessary oxygen is provided and excess carbon dioxide is removed from the water. If additional warmth is required, it can be supplied to the aquarium's inhabitants with a thermostatically controlled in-tank aquarium heater. An alternative method is to slightly elevate and position the tank over a heating pad. The bottom of the tank should be at least one centimeter (approximately one-half inch) above, and not actually touching, the pad. The top of the tank must be covered with a piece of glass or be furnished with a tightly fitting and escape-proof screened cover that can be fastened securely.

If water-dwelling spiders are kept, they should be fed small living fish that form a link in the food chain within a natural ecosystem.

2

Arachnids

Unlike their arthropod cousins, the insects, many arachnids do not go through metamorphosis between their juvenile and adult stages. However, some do require several molts of their nymphal chitinous exoskeleton before they assume the size of their adult parents; for example, some arachnids, particularly ticks and mites, do include an incomplete metamorphosis between the juvenile and adult stages.

The body of most arachnids is divided into two major parts: the *prosoma* consisting of a united head and thorax (sometimes called the "cephalothrorax"), and an *opisthosoma* (sometimes called an "abdomen"). The prosoma is formed from at least six body segments or *somites*, with each carrying a pair of appendages; these appendages may be chelicerae, pedipalps, or walking legs. The opisthosoma may have a maximum of thirteen somites; some of these somites can be found only in the embryonic arachnid because they become fused or otherwise lost in the adult form. Flattened plates, termed *tergites* on the prosoma are fused to form a "carapace" except in those orders of arachnids in which the tergites are separate. Matching ventral plates, called *sternites* cover most of the belly surface. In some arachnids, especially the solifugids, the last or caudal segment is formed by fusion of the respective sternite and tergite. In some, there is a distinct *mesosoma* composed of seven somites and a *metasoma* of five somites. In others, the caudal somites form a *pygidium*, or tall-like appendage (Savory 1964). The eighth somite contains the genital opening, or *gonopore*. The ninth and/or tenth somites contain the

Fig. 1, page 45

book lungs (**Figure 1**). These respiratory organs consist of thin layers of tissue over which air passes and oxygen and carbon dioxide are selectively exchanged. Not all arachnids possess book lungs; some exchange their respiratory gases through tube-like passages called "tracheae" that perforate their cuticle. A few others possess neither book lungs nor tracheae; they employ cutaneous respiration, having the gases diffuse directly across the semipermeable chitinous exoskeleton.

Most adult arachnids possess four pairs of walking legs. In those arachnids in which there are one or more immature or "nymphal" stages, the subadults are characterized by having only three pairs of walking legs. Baby spiders and scorpions look and behave much like their much larger adults. Also, most are capable of capturing the prey upon which they feed. Some arachnids lay eggs from which the young hatch after a variable period of incubation; others are born wrapped in a mantle of thin embryonic membranes. For example, scorpions are born alive and resemble their much larger parents. They are carried about for a variable period while clinging to their mother. Many female spiders attend their egg clutches and even aid their progeny in escaping the confines of the silken cocoon-like egg capsule. Young spiders appear like their parents except for their much smaller size and inability to reproduce.

In this book, eight of the sixteen orders of arachnids will be discussed. These are Araneida (spiders); Scorpiones (scorpions); Pseudoscorpiones ("false" or pseudoscorpions, "book scorpions"), Amblypygi, Palpigradi, Schizomida; Uropygi (whip scorpions); and Solifugae (sun, wind, or camel spiders).

Most spiders, scorpions, pseudoscorpions and whip scorpions have, in addition to their four pairs of walking legs, another pair of jointed appendages that are used for aiding in the capture and manipulation of prey and, in some, as a means for transferring semen; adult male spiders possess modified pedipalps that are equipped with hollow hook-like spines. The pedipalps of solifugids bear suction cup-like appendages called *arolia* which are employed in prey capture. Also, the solifugids, like no other arachnids, possess several pairs of trumpet horn or inverted funnel-shaped structures called "racket organs" attached to the posterio-ventral regions of the last pair of walking legs. These organs are believed to be sensitive to ground-borne vibrations.

The scorpions, pseudoscorpions, and whip scorpions have a pair of chelate pincer-like appendages similar to those found in some crabs and lobsters.

Of the arachnids discussed in this book, the spiders, pseudoscorpions, whip scorpions, and solifugids lay eggs; true scorpions bear living young which develop after a prolonged gestation period in the body of the fertilized female. Moreover, scorpions display impressive maternal care for their young. Also, solifugid females may exhibit great care for their newly hatched and only partially developed offspring, providing a steady supply of food to the nymph-like juveniles until they are able to fend for themselves.

"TARANTULAS" AND OTHER SPIDERS

"Will you walk into my parlour?" said the spider to the fly;
" 'Tis the prettiest little parlour that ever you did spy."
Mary Howitt
1799–1888

The term "tarantula" is derived from the folktales about the European spider, *Lycosa tarantula*, known as the Tarantula, and the lively dance, the tarantella, that was believed to be the antidote for the toxic effects experienced by those bitten by this common spider (**Figure 2**). The hairy mygalomorphs of the tropics and some temperate life zones are often called (mistakenly) "tarantulas."

Several species of tarantulas (*Aphonopelma eutylenum*; (**Figure 3**), *A. chalcodes; A. seemanni; Avicularia avicularia; Brachypelma smithi* (**Figure 4**), *Grammostola spathulata; Melopoeus albostriatus*) and related hairy orthognaths (mygalomorphs) such as the "bird-eating," "monkey," and "baboon" spiders are available from the commercial pet market. Recently, several tropical South American, African, and Asian rain forest and savannah dwelling species such as the baboon spiders (*Eucratiscelus longiceps; Ceratogyrus darlingi; Pterinochilus vorax; Citharischius crawshayi*) and the tropical

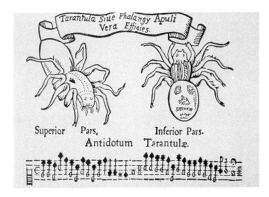

Figure 2. The first bars of the Tarantella, from an old Italian music manuscript, now in the Bettman Archive. Reprinted from Savory, 1961a.

Figure 3. California brown "tarantula," *Aphonopelma eutylenum*, more properly termed a mygalomorph or orthognath arachnid with its butterfly prey. These relatively common spiders make interesting study animals. The females are long lived in captivity.

Fig. 4, page 45

"tarantulas," (*Poecilotheria regalis* and *Pamphobetus antinous*) have been featured in monthly catalog sheets from several mail-order firms (some of which are noted at the end of this book). Other orthognaths, such as the trapdoor and funnel-web weaving spiders, can be caught in the wild in many locales in North America. To many, if not most, people, these creatures represent creepy, loathesome vermin; to others, they make very interesting, quiet, nonodoriferous pets and study animals, requiring minimal care. Some captive spiders were kept in order to gather their silk for optical reticule production; during World War II, black widow spiders yielded tough silk fiber for cross hairs used in bomb sights and sniper rifle scopesights. A U.S. Army scientist recently isolated the gene coding for the silk of the golden orb spider. These genes, which have been cloned and inserted into bacteria, which can now produce silk in mass quantities. This genetically engineered silk fiber has great potential in a variety of applications where its enormous tensile strength and light weight exceed those of steel or synthetic fibers.

Included in this discussion are the common garden orb-weaving spider (*Araneus* sp.); the fascinating trapdoor spider, (*Bothriocyrtum californicum*), that is so prevalent in the western United States; and the eastern trapdoor spider, (*Pachylomerus audouini*). These arachnids are predatory animals, employing a variety of hunting strategies. Some spin elaborate webs of fine silk; others spin sticky ground or surface webs to detect or entangle their prey; still others employ bola-like balls of sticky silk borne upon short threads of silk to ensnare the insects upon which they prey. Incredibly, these bola spiders also emit chemical substances that closely mimic the sex-attractant pheromones secreted by several species of female moths. These pheromone-rich scents are used to attract and then capture male moths. As the moth comes into the spider's range, it is ensnared by contact with the sticky bola. The spider then wraps silk about the moth to immobilize it, and sucks the body fluids and some soft tissues from the insect. Some of the orb-weaving spiders have only recently been found to spin webs whose ultraviolet light reflectances mimic those of flowers commonly visited by nectar-feeding insects; other spiders possess bodies that reflect ultraviolet light; thus, some insects are attracted to these spiders and their webs because they appear to be blossoms. It is also believed that these webs can deceive and entrap insects that fly toward open space. This is because the only other natural sources of ultraviolet light are the sun and daytime sky.

Most arachnids are solitary creatures; the majority will exhibit aggression or overt cannibalism when housed with their own kind. Though two or more spiders belonging to gregarious species may cooperate in the capture and the feeding upon a single prey insect (**Figure 5**), some "living space" is essential for territorial purposes. Compatible spiders may be housed together during the breeding season but even then the risk of acute population diminishment is ever present!

Except for the widow spiders (black widow, *Latrodectus mactans*; (**Figure 6**); northern widow, *L. variolus*; red-legged widow, *L. bishopi*; brown widow, *L. geometricus*); the brown recluse, *Loxosceles reclus* (**Figures 7a & b**); and the common brown spider, *L. unicolor*), the bulk of bites by North American spiders and tropical mygalomorph species pose little threat to humans except in unusually hypersensitive individuals. The tarantulas bite very infrequently and, even then, only in defense; such bites are usually inconsequential, causing no more problems than a bee sting would for most humans, dogs and cats. A more serious reaction can occur in individuals hypersensitive to the venom of these arachnids.

It is fascinating to observe the feeding behavior of many spiders. The common black widow spider displays a "memory"; if it is disturbed while feeding, it will retreat to a safe haven within its captive enclosure and then return to its meal when the disturbance is removed. It is also common for a 50–60 mg spider to subdue, kill, and feed upon a 3–5 gram mature sphinx moth! Similarly, the so-called "raft" spiders (*Dolomedes* sp.) can subdue, kill, and carry off small fish many times their own modest body weight.

Housing

Ground-dwelling "tarantulas" may be kept in a variety of terraria, glass or plastic fishbowls, or in

Fig. 5, page 45

Fig. 6, page 45

Fig. 7a, page 45

Fig. 7b, page 45

Fig. 8a, page 46

Fig. 8b, page 46

Fig. 9, page 46

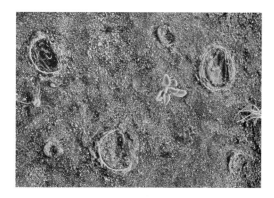

Figure 10a. A field of tubular nests of the California trapdoor spider, *Bothriocyrtum californicum*. In this photograph, the beveled lids are closed. Photo credit: Copyright 1933, Lee Passmore and the National Geographic Society.

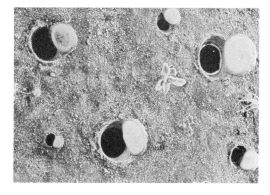

Figure 10b. The same field of nests with their lids opened. Photo credit: Copyright 1933, Lee Passmore and the National Geographic Society.

readily available gallon jars. Usually, they are incapable of ascending straight-sided, clean smooth glass surfaces. Both sexes spin ground webs rather than aerial webs so common to other spider-like arachnids. They should be kept by themselves. However, if more than one are housed in a large cage, adequate hiding places must be provided as refuges for escape or territorial sites. Large pieces of *nonresinous* bark, (oak, cherry, apple, pear, peach, apricot, almond, or other fruit or hardwood,) broken clay flower pot shards or similar objects should be furnished for such hiding places. Resinous woods such as pine, fir, cedar, redwood, etc. should be avoided. Tropical species require a more humid environment than those species whose native habitat is temperate.

The arboreal spiders, such as the common orb-weaving garden spiders (**Figures 8a & b**), make very interesting study animals and subjects for science projects. Because they spin elaborate concentric webs with which they entrap their insect prey, larger cage space is required than for the more sedentary tarantulas and trapdoor spiders. Either living plants or upright sticks must be provided from which the inhabitants can anchor their webs from point to point in their stereotyped fashion. The crab spiders prefer to lie in wait for their insect prey in the centers of composite flowers; their colors often mimics that of the flowers they inhabit (**Figure 9**). Other spiders, especially those of the genus *Argyroneta*, dive beneath the surface of fresh water and can be kept in small water-filled aquaria. The raft spider, *Dolomedes*, lives on the surface of small ponds and feeds upon insects and small fish and also may be housed in partially water-filled aquaria.

The ground-dwelling trapdoor spiders (**Figures 10a–f**) are believed by many to be the most interesting of the arachnids. For these, either a 38 liter (10 gallon) aquarium or glass jar should be filled with at least 20 cm (8 inches) of slightly moistened, salt-free loamy soil in which the spider can construct its tube-nest covered by a beveled trapdoor; the spider then lines both with smooth silk webbing. With luck, the spider will build its nest alongside one of the transparent walls. Completely covering the outside of an aquarium or jar with black paper enhances the like-

Figure 10c. The trapdoor covering the tubular nest is usually held closed with fangs of the the spider. Note the carefully beveled lid and its reciprocal tube which it covers. Copyright 1933, Lee Passmore and the National Geographic Society.

Figure 10e. A passing Jerusalem "cricket" is captured and dragged into the nest by a trapdoor spider. Copyright 1933, Lee Passmore and the National Geographic Society.

Figure 10f. A female trapdoor spider tending her brood of eggs laid at the bottom of a tubular nest excavated alongside the glass wall of a terrarium. Copyright 1933, Lee Passmore and the National Geographic Society.

lihood that the spider will construct its home next to one of the walls. Once the nest has been completed, the paper may be removed for observation of the spider's activities within its nest. In the case of trapdoor spiders, it is best not to furnish the cage with hiding places since these refuges will only inhibit the typical tube-nest building by these remarkable and industrious creatures.

Fig. 10d, page 46

Water

Although most, if not all, spiders obtain the majority of their moisture from the soft bodies of their prey, all will drink a surprising volume of water if it is provided in a readily available form. The "tarantulas" (mygalomorphs or othognaths), in particular, require fresh water to be present at all times to thrive in captivity (**Figure 11a**). A shallow glass or ceramic vessel should be placed on the surface of the sand or fine gravel cage litter. This water dish should be large enough to allow the spider to tilt itself easily onto the

Fig. 11a, page 46

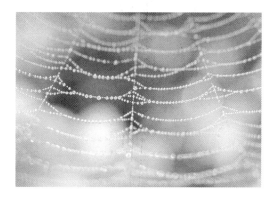

Figure 11b. Nature's jewels. Dew droplets strung like opalescent pearls on the web of the orb-weaving common garden spider, *Araneus*.

Fig. 12a, page 46

water's surface, but not so deep that the animal might topple in and, not being able to crawl out, drown. Another method is to place into the water a small piece of clean cellulose sponge from which the spider may imbibe its moisture, as required.

The webs of the orb web-weaving spiders may be lightly misted once daily to mimic dew drops, preferably at night or in early morning (**Figure 11b**). A hand-held household mist bottle is useful for this purpose. The entire cage should not become wet because too much moisture will facilitate the growth of disease causing bacteria and fungi.

Nutrition

The nutritional requirements of most common spiders and mygalomorphs are simple in comparison to those of many lower vertebrates. The ground-dwelling tarantulas and trapdoor spiders readily accept crickets, soft-bodied grubs, moths, and other winged insects (**Figure 12a**). Large Mexican and South American "bird-eating" mygalomorphs thrive on a diet of large crickets, grasshoppers, katydids, or newborn mouse pups. In their native habitat, some of these impressive arachnids do entrap and feed on small birds. These very large spiders and other tarantulas are somewhat inactive animals and should be fed about once weekly. The aerial web-weavers are far more active and, consequently, should be fed winged insects daily or at least two to five times each week. Their expenditure of energy in hunting and the production of protein-rich silk during the construction and maintenance of their webs is significant. Many spiders employ external or "extraoral" digestion; the prey's tissues are partially or fully liquefied by enzyme-rich salivary secretions that break down the body tissues of the prey. This liquid is then drawn up by the mouth parts of the spider, leaving behind a husk consisting of the now empty exoskeleton. Although some references state flatly that this is the only fashion by which all spiders ingest food, some, particularly the mygalomorphs, are capable of ingesting some solid tissue also, particularly when they are fed soft-bodied prey.

Houseflies and moths are a natural diet for the aerial web-weaving spiders. Moths can be easily attracted to outdoor lights in the evening hours, particularly if a blue light source is used. Small crickets can be substituted if they can be ensnared in an aerial web. Most spiders prefer or require living food, although recently dead insects may be substituted if they are held with forceps and made to wriggle in a web, thus inducing an attack by the spider.

Once entrapped in the web, an insect may be bitten and injected with a paralyzing venom, or the spider may spin a voluminous web about its prey, immobilizing it. Once the insect is wrapped in the restraining silken threads, its body fluids are drained by the spider. Tarantulas waste little energy in web-wrapping; the insect or mouse pup is held by the spider's pedipalps, envenomated with the fangs, and consumed. During the feeding process, the spider's abdomen may increase to as much as three times its pre-dining volume. When feeding upon very large prey such as a mouse pup or sphinx moth, the meal may require as much as two days to be completed.

The major excretory waste product of protein digestion in arachnids is composed largely of guanine microcrystals. Freshly deposited guanine is excreted as a slurry and has the appearance of a pasty white or light tan material (**Figure 12b**) which soon hardens to a firm chalk-like consistency. Under normal weekly feeding schedules, guanine is passed at approximately two-week intervals. Because it is relatively insoluble and may accumulate under conditions of metabolic dehydration, sufficient water must always be available to ensure that captive arachnids do not become "constipated."

Fig. 12b, page 47

Reproduction

The sexes of spiders are determined by the smaller size of the cephalothorax, longer legs, and bulbous pedipalps of the male. Compare **Figures 7a & b** and **8a & b**. The highly developed and bulbous pedipalps of males bear short spines that are employed in the tranfer of spermatozoa to the female. These large pedipalps can be seen even in small spiders and are a useful means for distinguishing male from female spiders.

Mygalomorphs, after completing their courtship ritual, approach each other frontally. Previously, the male had constructed a special "sperm web" onto which he ejaculated and transferred a mass of his semen to his pedipalps. Here the spermatozoa enter reservoirs at the bases of the pedipalpal spines by being drawn up via capillary action. As the tarantulas approach each other, they raise the forward portions of their bodies. The male places the tips of his pedipalps into the female's genital opening on the mid-underside of her body, approximately midway between her mouthparts and her spinerets. The spermatozoa are transferred to her seminal recepticles, where they are stored until needed to fertilize her eggs. After mating, if he does not escape swiftly, the male may be devoured by the female. This is not a consistent behavior, but when it does occur it provides a ready meal for the female requiring little expenditure of energy on her part.

Male and female mygalomorphs both reach sexual maturity at approximately seven years of age, but the males are genetically "programmed" to die after their seventh year; in contrast, females may live for as long as twenty-five to thirty years in properly managed captivity. Parenthetically, most of the common brown or black California "tarantulas" found crossing expanses of open soil or paved roads are mature seven-year-old males seeking mates; the females tend to wander much less, preferring to remain close to their shallow burrows and rocky crevices, or beneath slabs of loose tree bark. The males almost invariably will die within a month or two following their last (seventh year) molt, despite the excellent captive care they may receive.

Usually, the gravid spider deposits her eggs in a nest spun from her silk. Most species spin a flat web composed of closely woven and cross-linked fibers. The edges are brought together until an almost spherical encasement is formed in which the eggs are confined. When the final eggs that are to be deposited in the clutch are passed, the female then closes the last remaining opening in the cocoon-like egg case.

The females of some species remain very close to

their egg masses until the hatching spiderlets are
ready to emerge (**Figure 13**); some carry their broods
of eggs around with them. A developing black widow
spider embryo is illustrated in **Figure 14**. In those species who attend their egg cases, it is likely that the
female can sense minute vibrations produced by the
newly hatched spiders. In *Latrodectus* (and probably
other genera), the attending female chews a small hole
in the silken brood case, or secretes a silk-dissolving
enzyme that serves to soften the area to which it is
applied. This behavior facilitates the escape of the
young spiderlets (**Figure 15**).

Studies of the common western black widow spider, *Latrodectus mactans hesperus*, in my laboratory
(Frye, unpublished data) indicated that wild-caught
females were able to produce multiple fertile egg
masses for periods exceeding one year without having
had additional physical contact with mature males.
These spiders were kept in strict isolation. Some egg
masses were either sampled at various times during
the incubation period (approximately thirty-four
days) and subjected to routine histologic processing
and microscopic examination; others were allowed to
develop to hatching. The answer to whether this period of prolonged fertility represents the retention
of spermatozoa long after the last possible mating
(which is termed *amphigonia retardata*), or merely virgin birth or *parthenogenesis*, had to await the sexing of
the progeny as they matured and completed their
adult molt. That much awaited event occurred, and it
is now clear that amphigonia retardata *is*, indeed, the
mechanism because each of several clutches contained
males. If it were due to parthenogenesis, all the progeny would have been females. Thus, rather than im-
maculate *conception*, these animals practice immacu-
late *deception*! After the first adult ecdysis, the males
could be identified by their sexually dimorphic large,
bulbous pedipalps (**Figure 16**); a few males were re-
tained for future breeding to mature females.

Medical Disorders

Other than the previously mentioned dehydration or starvation from lack of suitable food, the spi-

Fig. 13, page 47

Fig. 14, page 47

Fig. 15, page 47

Fig. 16, page 47

Fig. 17a, page 47

Fig. 17b, page 48

Fig. 17c, page 48

Fig. 18, page 48

Fig. 19a, page 48

Fig. 19b, page 48

ders are remarkably free of disease. The mygalomorph tarantulas often will exhibit dorsal abdominal alopecia, or baldness, related to the loss of specialized body hairs (**Figures 4, 17a**). These "urticarial hairs" are employed as a defense mechanism; when disturbed, the tarantula uses its hind pair of legs to flick these short, stiff hairs, which are extremely irritating to the eyes and skin of a potential predator or antagonist.

Periodically, the old epidermis is molted. This process is termed *ecdysis*. During the early stages of ecdysis, a "molting fluid" is secreted between the old cuticle and the newly formed epidermal products. This enzyme-rich fluid serves two purposes: it moistens and partially digests the inner cuticle whose constituents are recycled to the new integument, and it aids in lubricating the two surfaces as it exerts a hydraulic force upon the old cuticle which helps split it along the edge of the prosoma and the lower surface of the opisthosoma. The "carapace" falls away, and as the animal shrugs out of its old exoskeleton, the worn coat shrivels (**Figures 17b & c**).

After molting, the urticarial hairs as well as the other body hairs are replaced fully; pedipalpi, walking legs, and even the fangs and ocelli or "corneae" of the eight eyes are renewed (**Figure 18**). Some arachnids turn themselves over on their backs to facilitate the ecdysis; others are able to accomplish this necessary process while maintaining a normal posture. Molting the entire exoskeleton may require one to several hours to be completed. Under conditions of insufficient humidity, some mygalomorphs experience difficulty in molting their old exoskeleton. One or more applications of finely misted water to the old cuticle or epidermal remnants of the partially shed exoskeleton often will soften it and resolve the problem.

Occasionally, an anxious owner will try to hasten the process of molting and, in doing so, will dismember one or more legs from the cephalothorax (**Figure 19a**). Clear, slightly viscous hemolymph, which is analogous to blood, will ooze from the limb stumps (**Figure 19b**) and can be staunched by applying a drop or two of cyanomethacrylate glue ("Super Glue," "Crazy Glue," etc.). If the creature survives such dismemberment, its legs usually will regenerate after one or more subsequent molts.

Obvious wounds should be flushed with an appropriate *aqueous* antibiotic solution after cytological or microbiological examination of any exudate has yielded results that confirm bacterial infection.

Chemical restraint or anesthesia may be readily accomplished by confining the spider or spider-like arachnid to a glass or clear plastic container in which a volatile anesthetic agent has been introduced. Ether, methoxyflurane, halothane, and isoflurane have produced excellent results. Great care must be taken with ether fumes because they are explosive. Ideally, these anesthetic gases should be delivered by a calibrated closed-circuit anesthetic machine, rather than being adminstered by placing the animal in a glass container with a volatile fluid-soaked cotton ball or gauze sponge. This will help prevent a fatal overdosage. Cooper (1987) also mentioned employing hypothermia, but this modality should be reserved for restraint only because there is reason to doubt whether cold alone will abolish pain.

Both internal and external parasites may infest spiders, but their control or treatment may pose an equal threat to the host. External mite infestation is treated by anesthetizing the spider with an inhalant agent such as isoflurane or halothane and then removing the mites by brushing the spider gently with a camel's hair brush. This may have to be repeated several times to remove every parasite, but the technique is safe and effective.

Parasitic wasps particularly the genus *Pepsis* (**Figure 20a**) and their developing larvae are, potentially, the most serious threat to mygalomorphs and other large spiders. The egg laying female wasp stings the spider, injecting it with its paralyzing venom. This does not kill the spider but immobilizes it. The wasp then deposits one or more fertilized eggs onto the surface of the prostrate spider, which now serves as a ready food source for the developing wasp larva(e). This wasp predation may be prevented by screening the cage to prevent wasps' access to the spider.

Household insecticides must, of course, be kept away from captive spiders and other arachnids and insects. Once poisoned, there is no specific treatment.

The cage environment should be kept clean to prevent infestation with pathogenic or parasitic organisms. Except for drinking water or a daily light

Fig. 20a, page 48

misting of any aerial webs, excessive moisture must be avoided.

Rarely, tumors or other masses of abnormal tissue develop in arachnids, particularly older ones. As this text was going through the final stages of editing, the author had the opportunity to examine a very old Mexican red-kneed tarantula, *Brachypelma smithii* with a growth which had first been noticed by its owner three months previously. The mass appeared to have originated from the opening of the left third book lung (**Figures 20b–c**). The growth consisted of golden-brown water- and lipid-insoluble pigment deposits and was found to have displaced several of the spider's internal organs. After review by several comparative pathologists, the mass was diagnosed as a form of chronic granuloma that arose in response to trauma. The pigment is thought to be melanin or melanin-related.

Fig. 20b, page 49

Fig. 20c, page 49

SCORPIONS

That was the Africa we knew,
Where, wandering alone,
We saw, heraldic in the heat,
A scorpion on a stone.

William Plomer
1903–

One would rarely consider a scorpion as a "pet," but they have been kept as captives to study their life habits and the biological effects of their complex venoms. Recently, southwestern desert hairy scorpions, *Hadrurus arizonensis, H. hirsutus* (**Figures 21a & b**), and large black African emperor scorpions, *Pandinus imperator* (**Figure 22a**), Israeli gold scorpions, *Scorpio mauris*, Java scorpions, *Heterometrus cyaneus*, and the impressive Asian black scorpions, particularly *Palamnaeus fulvipes*, have entered the pet trade and have found welcome homes in many localities. These arachnids characteristically have eight walking legs, highly specialized pincer-like claws on the pedipalps, (**Figure 22b**) and an elongated, segmented metasoma or "tail" bearing a bulbous telson with its recurved hollow needle-like sting. The sting eventually becomes dulled with continued use, and it is renewed

Fig. 21a, page 49

Fig. 21b, page 49

Fig. 22a, page 49

Fig. 22b, page 49

during each molting cycle. Scorpions alone among the arachnids possess angled comb-like "pectines" that are located immediately behind the last pair of walking legs (see **Figure 21b**). These interesting organs are thought to serve as "sonotactic" or vibration receptors, sensitive to ground-transmitted vibratory stimuli. Laboratory evidence has also substantiated a chemosensory function for these organs (Stahnke 1966); scorpions could detect dead insects when their pectines came into contact with them. Scorpions breathe through four pairs of book lungs whose openings are in the ninth and tenth somites on the ventral surface of the mesosoma. These internal gill-like organs function as lungs in higher animals and were described previously. Like spiders, scorpions molt their exoskeletons periodically (**Figure 22g**).

Scorpions are represented in the fossil record. The oldest, *Paleosphonus nuncius*, was found in sediments dating from the Silurian Period, which existed approximately 390 million years before the present. Most of the prehistoric scorpions were substantially larger than current species; one, *Gigantoscorpio willsi*, that lived during the late Paleozoic Age, measured 35 cm (13.8 inches) in length.

Most of the New World, North African, and Asian scorpions are not particularly hazardous to humans. Exceptions are several species of the North American genus *Centruroides*; the Brazilian *Tityus*; and the North African *Androctonus*; the European, Middle Eastern and North African *Buthus*, *Parabuthus*, *Mesobuthus*, and *Leiurus*; and the Indo-Pakistani *Buthotus*. However, the sting of even "harmless" species can result in pain and, sometimes, localized loss of tissue. The European scorpion *Buthus* sp. and the previously mentioned hairy scorpions, *Hadrurus hirsutus* and *H. arizonensis*, common to the western United States, are suitable for study animals. They are hardy and adapt well to captivity, often living for three or more years. Some do not achieve sexual maturity until their seventh year.

Scorpions may be safely and humanely picked up by their metasoma with long thumb forceps or similar instruments; if they are going to be kept in captivity, they should be deposited into suitable jars or other containers from which they may not escape or sting

Fig. 22g, page 50

Fig. 22c, page 50

Fig. 22d, page 50

Fig. 22e, page 50

Fig. 22f, page 50

the unwary. Handling may be stressful to them and, therefore, should be limited to necessary situations only and then with gentleness.

Scorpions exhibit bright tourqoise fluorescence when viewed with ultraviolet "black" light illumination (**Figures 22d–f**). This exoskeletal fluorescence develops in the chitin of newborn scorpions only after one or more molts and is present in the old cast-off sheds. Whether there could be a selective advantage conferred by ultraviolet fluorescence remains a mystery because these creatures are largely nocturnal and, therefore, sources of natural ultraviolet illumination would be lacking at night. However, this characteristic is a highly conserved trait that is found in most, if not all species of scorpions from the old and new worlds. The flurorescence makes finding these illusive beasties easier to spot at night when a battery-operated source of ultraviolet light is used to illuminate the desert soil, rocks, and detritus from which these animals emerge after dark.

Housing

Scorpions are common inhabitants of weathered woodpiles, rock slides and old pieces of fallen tree bark. Like their cousins, the spiders and solifugids, scorpions tend to be solitary creatures and should not be housed together except for breeding. They may be kept in smooth-sided glass or plastic jars or small terraria fitted with escape-proof lids.

The cage or jar should be furnished with a sandy or loamy soil litter or substrate in which the scorpion may dig its shallow burrows, usually beneath a flat stone or piece of flower pot shard. Dry, well-weathered bark is also acceptable as a hiding place during the day for these usually nocturnal or crepuscular secretive creatures.

Water

Although scorpions derive most of their fluid intake from their prey, they will readily drink from shallow containers of fresh water (**Figure 22c & 22f**).

Nutrition

Captive scorpions should be fed soft-bodied grubs, crickets, moths, or small spiders. The larger, more tropical species should be fed cockroaches or mouse pups. Occasionally, a large spider may devour the scorpion, but this is uncommon unless the prey spider is considerably larger than the resident host. Tiny newborn scorpions do not feed until they have molted at least once and leave the safety of their mothers' backs. As soon as they become independent, they feed upon correspondingly small prey such as "pinhead" crickets, newly hatched silk moth larvae, genetically wingless fruit flies, termites, or other tiny insects, grubs, or spiders.

When attacking, the scorpion grasps its prey with one or both of its pincer-like claws and, bringing its sting-tipped telson up and over its back, inserts the sharp point into a soft spot and injects a small amount of venom. Once immobilized, the prey is brought to the mouth area and the sharp-edged chitinous chelicerae are employed in tearing the soft body parts from the victim. Some references state that only the fluid portions of the prey are ingested, but this is erroneous; many scorpions masticate and swallow nearly all of their prey insects and spiders. Even the chitinous outer body parts are triturated and ingested (**Figures 23a–c**).

Generally, scorpions are fed once every other week. Several published accounts have documented extended fasts lasting well over a year; in fact, there is evidence that the overly well-fed scorpion lives a shorter life than one that has been less well provided with food. Very active specimens may require more frequent feeding. Scorpions usually refuse to feed just prior to ecdysis and for a day or two after they have shed their old exoskeleton. Once the freshly renewed cuticle hardens their appetite returns.

Although scorpions are solitary creatures, the young of some species such as *Pandinus imperator* will remain in sibling groups for some period of time after they leave the safety of their mother's back. When kept together, they often tolerate each other as they mature into adulthood. When kept under such con-

Fig. 23a, page 50

Fig. 23b, page 51

Fig. 23c, page 51

ditions, they will even share meals. Other species, are much less tolerant and will cannibalize their own kind.

Reproduction

Although parthenogenesis has been documented in some scorpions, the majority of species include separate sexes. Most scorpions possess an XY chromasome sex-determining system, but in some species, the male gametes may carry two to four X chromosomes, rather the single one found in most other animals whose sex is determined by a heterogametic system. During a courtship "dance," a male scorpion deposits a packet of semen, called a *spermatophore*, onto the ground over which he maneuvers a receptive female. The spermatophore enters the female's genital opening and is stored in specialized structures called *spermathecae*. Fertilization occurs during the egg-laying process; the spermatozoa are released from the spermathecae and enter each egg as they descend the oviduct, before the outer membranes are deposited. Gestation requires nearly one year. Interestingly, the young are born alive, rather than emerging from externally hatched eggs. The developing embryos are furnished with little or no yolk; early in their development, each embryo attaches to an outpouching of the oviduct from which they absorb hemolymph from the maternal circulation and thereby derive their energy and nutrients during gestation. This is loosely analogous to the embryonic-fetal nutrition of higher animals possessing more complicated placentas. The full-term baby scorpions are born surrounded by a thin membrane. The newborn scorpions are miniatures replicas of their parents. Some scorpions flex their anterior-most limbs to form a "birth basket" into which the young are delivered (Keegan 1980). The young almost immediately climb onto the female scorpion's back (**Figures 24**). In some species, the distribution of the newborn is highly ordered; in others it is not and the nymphs are stacked several deep. Usually baby scorpions are carried on the mother's back for several days to three weeks or more. While they are tolerant of each others' presence dur-

Fig. 24, page 51

ing this time, after leaving their maternal conveyance and protective influence, they may attack and devour each other as the occasion arises.

Medical Disorders

Other than filth- and moisture-enhanced bacterial and fungal diseases, scorpions rarely exhibit overt illness. As they become senescent, they gradually eat less often and eventually die of old age. Some species have lived in captivity for as long as several years. Like spiders, to which they are related, scorpions molt their exoskeletons as they grow and as the old cuticle wears out. Ecdysis usually requires about an hour or two and usually is accomplished at night. The old epidermis splits along the back of the cephalothorax, abdomen, and tail. Once the old exoskeleton is loosened, the scorpion wriggles free and crawls out of its old "skin." Missing limbs may be regenerated after several molts. Until the chitin of the new exoskeleton hardens (which requires a few hours), the scorpion is prone to injury and predation.

Scorpions occasionally become infested with parasitic mites. The treatment for these parasites is identical as that employed with mite infestation in large spiders: the scorpion is placed into a jar and a carefully controlled mixture of oxygen and a 3–4% volatile, nonflammable anesthetic agent is introduced. When the scorpion becomes torpid, it is gently brushed with a camel's hair paint brush to remove the drowsy mites. Afterwards, the scorpion is removed from the anesthetic atmosphere and permitted to awaken fully and resume its activities.

Most species of scorpions thrive at moderate temperatures from 18–19 °C to 32 °C (64–89.6 °F); others can tolerate higher or lower extremes, but most will exhibit heat stress at environmental temperatures exceeding 35 °C (95 °F). Direct exposure to unfiltered sunlight will quickly overheat them unless they can enter an area of shelter and shade.

Newborn scorpions occasionally experience difficulty freeing themselves from the thin embryonic membranes in which they are wrapped at birth (**Figure 25a**). Once these membranes become dried, they

Figure 25a. Occasionally, not all of the scorpions are able to free themselves from their birth membranes. Illustrated are seven baby scorpions thought to have been "stillborn." They are still tucked up and enshrouded by their thin, dried birth membranes.

Figure 25b. Less than 7 minutes after they were moistened with water, the tiny scorpions are beginning to free themselves from the imprisoning membranes.

Fig. 26, page 51

imprison the infant arachnid; after a period of unproductive struggle, the tiny scorpion becomes exhausted and dies. If observed in time, the baby scorpion can be freed by moistening the membrane, which permits the animal to free itself and crawl away (**Figure 25b**). In some instances, gentle teasing away of the adherant membranes may be required. Other scorpions are free of their birth membranes before they emerge from the female's genital pore.

PSEUDOSCORPIONS AND WHIP SCORPIONS

Pseudoscorpions and whip scorpions generally are smaller than most true scorpions. The largest whip scorpions rarely exceed 10 cm (4 inches) in total length, and most pseudoscorpions are even smaller, usually only a few millimeters long; some species exceed several centimeters, but these are the exceptions. One of the largest is *Mastigoproctus giganteus*. For the sake of brevity, the orders of pseudoscorpions Amblypygi, Schizomida, and Uropygi will be discussed together because their habits are so similar.

Whip scorpions are often called "vinegaroons" because of their ability to squirt small streams of acetic acid at adversaries or potential predators. Members of the Uropygi can also secrete formic acid. These invertebrates accommodate the curious by delivering a strong vinegar-smelling attack when disturbed; although highly aromatic, this secretion is harmless to humans. Whip scorpions bear the large pincer-like pedipalps so characteristic of true scorpions, but lack the sting-tipped bulbous telson at the end of a long jointed tail; their caudal appendage is little more than a thin rearward-facing antenna-like "whip" metasoma (**Figure 26**). Some whip scorpions lack a tail altogether, and members of the order Schizomida possess only a very short metasoma or "telson." These arachnids possess markedly long walking legs; generally, their pedipalps are less well developed than those of tailed whip scorpions. Although equipped with venom glands and ducts and tiny pincer-like pedipalpal chelae, which are only a fraction of a centi-

meter long, these tiny pseudoscorpions do not pose
a threat to humans (**Figures 27**).

Fig. 27, page 51

The chelicerae of pseudoscorpions are equipped
with silk glands that are used during the mating process; the males spin a gradually tapering web-like
structure, into which the female is lured to take up
the spermatophore. Pseudoscorpions breath via tracheae that open through the cuticle of the opisthosoma or midsection.

Some of the smaller pseudoscorpions distribute
themselves within their environment by a process
called *phoresy*, which involves attaching themselves to
flying insects, birds or even small mammals and
"hitching a ride" to a new location. If the chauffeur
is small enough to be overcome, it may be attacked
and devoured by its erstwhile passenger after alight-
ing in a new location. Other species are most commonly found in libraries, where they live in old book
bindings and subsist on small paper-eating insects
and grain or dust mites.

Housing

Whip scorpions and pseudoscorpions are kept in
woodland terraria in much the same manner as the
true scorpions, centipedes, and millipedes. The tini-
est pseudoscorpions should be kept in Petri dishes or
small vials furnished with paper or forest litter and a
substrate of clean sand that can be moistened to provide necessary humidity. Because they are often secretive in their habits, larger pseudoscorpions should
be provided with some refuge in the form of one or
more pieces of nonresinous tree bark or shards of a
broken flower pot. Living plants will make the enclosure more aesthetically pleasing. Unlike true scorpions, which are solitary creatures except when
seeking to mate, pseudoscorpions are often found in
the company of their peers. Some may live for only a
year, while others can be kept for two or even three
years.

Water

Moisture is largely obtained from the tissue fluid
of the whip scorpion or pseudoscorpion's prey, but a

twice-weekly light spray of fresh water applied to the foliage in the enclosure is recommended to furnish small droplets from which these creatures can drink. A household hand-held spray bottle is useful for this twice-weekly misting.

Nutrition

Whip scorpions eat much the same diet as their true scorpion cousins, but on a smaller scale. Pseudoscorpions, because of their diminutive size, subsist on very small soil and dust-dwelling creatures. Depending upon their age, growth rate, and size, whip scorpions and pseudoscorpions should be fed small insects or spiders twice weekly. Like their much larger true scorpion kin, they can endure prolonged fasts.

Reproduction

Whip scorpions and pseudoscorpions reach sexual maturity at ages ranging from several months up to three years. Fertilization is internal. After an appropriate courtship "dance" during which the male grasps the female's pincers, he maneuvers her over a stalked spermatophore that he has fastened to the substrate. Often a special web called a "spermatophore web" is spun from silk produced by glands in the male's pincer-like pedipalps and attached to overhanging objects, which leads the female into the proximity of the spermatophore. The semen contained in or on the surface of the spermatophore enters the female's genital orifice or gonopore where the spermatozoa fertilize the ripe eggs within the oviducts. Just before the fertilized eggs pass out through the gonopore, a substance is secreted by specialized glands near the genital orifice. This substance forms a membrane which forms an incubation chamber into which the eggs are deposited. This membrane is not detached from the oviduct; rather, it serves as a communication between the internal maternal environment and the external brood chamber; the embryos are nourished with "false scorpion milk" that is conveyed from the maternal haemocoel via the tubular membrane. When the term embyro is ready to leave the incubation chamber, it molts its exoskeleton and the first neonatal stage, called a *protonymph* emerges. Later two other stages, accompanied by molts occur. These are the *deutonymph*, and *tritonymph*. After a final "larval" molt, the tritonymph becomes an adult. Thus, the development and juvenile morphology of pseudoscorpions differs substantially and is far more complex than the true scorpions.

Medical Disorders

Other than occasional mite infestations, whip scorpions and pseudoscorpions are rarely affected by disease. Like many arthropods, they can be infected with *Bacillus thuringienensis* and some fungi, especially under conditions of an over moist or filthy environment.

SUN SPIDERS (SOLIFUGIDS)

These hairy spider-like arachnids, often called "sun," "wind," or "camel" spiders lack a constricted waist dividing the body into leg-bearing prosoma and an abdomen-like opisthosoma; rather, the opisthosoma is fitted with flattened transverse plate-like segments, called *tergites*, on the back are similar plates, called *sternites*, that cover the belly (**Figure 28a & b**). Each of the pedipalps is much more heavily developed than any of the four pairs of walking legs and is equipped with a suction cup structure called an *arolium*, which is employed in capturing and manipulating prey. The opisthosoma ends in a circular segment. There is no "tail" or mesosoma such as is found in scorpions. Large paired median eyes or *ocelli* are located just behind the huge jaws which are termed *chelate chelicerae*. Often these chelicerae are enormous and wedge-shaped and may account for as much as one-third of the animals' total length. Relative to the size of these animals, these immense jaws are some of the most powerful in the Animal Kingdom. Sun spiders are highly effective predators which subdue their insect, arachnid, and even small vertebrate prey without venom. Instead, after a rushed

Fig. 28a, page 51

Fig. 28b, page 52

attack during which they clutch the victim in their legs, they crush it with their massive jaws. The tissue fluids and soft body parts of the prey are then swallowed.

The cuticle is furnished with stiff hair-like setae some of which probably serve as airborne vibration-detecting, auditory sense organs. This ability to to sense and behaviorally respond to vibrations is called *sonotaxis*. As mentioned previously, the solifugids also possess specialized vibration sensing structures called "racket organs" that apparently are sensitive to ground vibrations. These appendages consist of several pairs of inverted funnel-shaped objects that are attached to the rear pair of walking legs. Solifugids are most often found in arid or semiarid life zones, although some species have been found in far more moist habitats.

Sun spiders vary in length from as little as 1 cm (less than one-half inch) to about 5 cm (2-inches). Because of their speed and ability to deliver a painful but venomless bite, it is best to handle solifugids remotely by inducing them to enter wide-mouth jars or nets from which they can be transferred to other escape-proof containers.

Housing

Sun spiders are kept in terraria or large open-mouth glass or plastic jars fitted with lids perforated with small ventilation holes. Dry sand or coarse gravel is used as litter material, and a curved piece of bark or pottery shard serves as a refuge. Most sun spiders thrive at moderate room temperatures and will benefit from brief exposure to natural sunshine. Great care must be given to prevent overheating of the terrarium or jar during these sunbaths.

Water

Although they receive a large proportion of their moisture from the body fluids of their prey, solifugids will also imbibe water from shallow vessels in their environment.

Reproduction

Although male sun spiders lack a penile organ, fertilization in these arachnids is internal and similar to that employed in true spiders. After a cautious courtship, the male deposits semen onto the ground and, after picking it up with his chelicerae, turns the female onto her side and deposits it into her reproductive opening, the gonopore. After this process, the male retreats quickly before his mate recovers from her amorous torpor and regains her usual feeding habits. Within a few days, the gravid female excavates a burrow into which she deposits 100 or more eggs. The newly hatched young solifugids are only incompletely formed. The alimentary, excretory, and respiratory systems are immature or lacking altogether. After its first molt, the young solifugid becomes a protonymph. Following growth and several molts, these nymphal stages finally assume the adult characteristics of their parents.

Medical Disorders

These creatures are remarkably free of disease, and under satisfactory captive husbandry may live for over one year. Earlier death may result from traumatic injury or sporadic bacterial infections. Another hazard is attacks by *Pepsis* wasps (**see Figure 20a**), which sometimes end in the death of the wasps.

3

Chilopods and Diplopods

CENTIPEDES

The centipede was happy quite
Until the toad in fun
Said, "Pray, which leg goes after which?"

That worked her mind to such a pitch,
She lay distracted in a ditch,
Considering how to run.

Mrs. Edward Craster
Pinafore Poems, 1871.

With a segmented body characterized by the presence of a single pair of jointed legs per segment, the Class Chilopoda represents centipedes, the so-called "100-legged" beings. Thousands of individual species of centipedes inhabit North, Central and South America, thriving in temperate, arid and tropical life zones. Some centipedes are minute creatures, while others, like *Scolopendra* sp., may be more than 16 cm (6–7 inches) long when fully grown (**Figure 29**); the red-headed centipede, *Copris texanum* grows to a length of 20 cm (8 inches). Most are predatory, feeding upon soft-bodied arthropods and small vertebrates such as amphibians, lizards, small snakes, birds, and small mammals. The scutigerid forms like *Scutigera coleoptera* possess only seventeen pairs of legs, but these limbs are elongated and more spider-like than

Figure 29. A centipede. Although these creatures do not actually possess 100 legs as their name implies, they do have many pairs. The larger centipedes can deliver a very painful bite to the unwary.

31

Figure 30. A scutigerid centipede. This family of chilopods differs from other centipedes in possessing long jointed antennae, 17 pairs of very long, spider-like limbs, and round compound eyes, similar to those of insects. These arthropods can move very swiftly and are secretive in their habits.

those of most other centipedes (**Figure 30**); these forms differ also in possessing large compound eyes and long antennae that are similar to those found in insects. Some larger Asian centipedes imported into the United States can attack, kill, and devour adult mice! Their prey are attacked and bitten using a pair of horizontally opposed, recurved fangs. These fangs can inflict painful bites if they penetrate the skin of a person's unprotected fingers or toes.

As they grow, the centipedes periodically shed their old, outgrown exoskeletons, much in the fashion of the scorpions and spiders.

Some centipedes have lived for over three years in captivity, but most species complete their life cycles in about one year.

Housing

Depending upon the habitat from which the centipedes were obtained, they may be kept in terraria filled to a depth of about 5 cm (2 inches) of dry sand, loamy soil or forest litter over which a few pieces of tree bark or clay pot shards are scattered to provide shelter. These animals will usually burrow beneath these refuges and range out during periods of subdued light to hunt for prey or mates. Some species are cannibalistic and, if kept with each other, must be afforded adequate hiding places and territory. Overcrowding will result in the loss of animals until only a single centipede remains. In public exhibits, the larger centipedes are housed separately. An ambient temperature of 26–28 °C (78.8–82.4 °F) generally is adequate to maintain health. The humidity varies with the species; arid dwelling taxa require a far drier climate than those originating from the tropical rainforest life zones.

Nutrition

Most species of centipedes will thrive on a captive diet of soft-bodied grubs, winged insects, spiders and (for the larger individuals) mouse pups. Feeding frequency depends on their size, growth pattern, and the nature of their meals. Those fed mice need eat only about once weekly; those eating insects should be fed once or twice weekly.

Water

Like the spiders and scorpions, centipedes obtain most of their dietary moisture from the body fluids of their prey. They will, however, drink fresh water from containers (which should be shallow enough to allow escape should they topple in accidentally).

Reproduction

Centipedes mate via the transfer of semen, which is deposited by the male onto a silken web or in a spermatophore; the female enters the web and takes up the fresh ejaculate with her mandibles and places it into her genital opening. Fertilized eggs are deposited into burrows where the female may coil about her brood as they develop and eventually hatch. The young centipedes are tiny copies of their parents and may attack each other, if the opportunity presents itself. Usually they feed on whatever small arthropods they can overcome.

MILLIPEDES

Another arthropod class, Diplopoda (the millipedes), has become an object of interest to the pet trade and their clientele in the last few years. The domestic species that have evolved in the temperate life zone are usually too small to excite any but the most enthusiastic fans, but the tropical and subtropical millipedes, native to the world's rain forests, are far more robust and have attracted attention. They often are up to 17–20 cm (7–8 inches) in length and over 1 cm (1/2 inch) in diameter. Usually black or rust-colored, these shiny creatures have two pairs of jointed limbs attached to and moving with each of the body segments posterior to the head. Forward motion is accomplished by moving these legs in a progressive wave-like fashion. These fascinating animals possess

Fig. 31a, page 52

Fig. 31b, page 52

two major defense mechanisms when disturbed by a potential predator: when touched or threatened, they immediately writhe away from their tormentor and roll into a tight coil (**Figure 31a**). If this maneuver fails to disuade the aggressor, the millipede exudes a foul-smelling, often acrid fluid from its vent. This fluid is harmless to unbroken skin, but is unpleasant. Although millipedes do not bite when handled (**Figure 31b**), the hands should be washed thoroughly after contact with these creatures.

While they are hardly a cuddly pet, many-legged millipedes make interesting, easily kept study animals for students of biology. With proper care, they may live seven or more years. Once they have reached their adult size after one or more years, their growth slows markedly, although they may continue to grow slightly throughout life.

Housing

Because millipedes are dwellers among vegetable debris and forest litter, their captive habitats should reflect their reclusive preferences. They may be kept in glass or plastic terraria furnished with a layer of well-rotted leaf mold or similar material. Flat stones or pieces of weathered tree bark should be placed in the terrarium so that the millipedes can seek shelter beneath them.

The ambient temperature at which these creatures are kept does not appear to be critical, but should range between 20–30 °C (68–86 °F). The cage environment should be slightly humid. This may be accomplished by placing a piece of glass or similar impervious materal over the top of the habitat.

Nutrition

Fig. 31c, page 52

Millipedes tend to be opportunistic in their dietary preferences. They thrive on a diet of garden vegetables, fresh apple slices (**Figure 31c**), and a small amount of commercial dog, cat, or pelleted fish food or poultry feed. Commercial fish food tablets such as

Tetra Tabi Min are eaten avidly by these creatures. Tabi Min is available from most aquarium and pet stores in the United States and Europe. Those nutrients that may be mildly deficient in vegetable material can be supplemented by the dry poultry mash or fish food tablets.

The food choices are provided *ad lib*. The larger millipedes tend to feed daily and may consume nearly half their weight in moist food every 24 hours! They can withstand going without food for two to three weeks, but this is not recommended.

Water

Most of the ingested water that millipedes absorb is derived from moisture contained in the vegetable matter in their diet. A ration of drier food items will necessitate a greater need for water. If water is available as fine misted droplets, these animals will drink from leaves and other objects in their path. Containers of standing water are not necessary because millipedes usually do not drink from them; also, they may topple in and cannot crawl out of steep-sided vessels.

Reproduction

Sexual maturity may take as long as three years with the larger species of millipedes. Fertilization is internal. Sexual dimorphism, if present, often is subtle except to enthusiastic millipede observers—and other millipedes! Once the fertilized eggs are mature, they are laid in a nest beneath a fallen log or similar protected site. In some species of millipedes, the female usually remains with her egg clutch; in other species, the female carries her eggs from place to place in a pouch-like space beneath her belly and formed by her inward directed legs. The millipede arches her back in a way that keeps the inactive legs forming the pouch from touching the ground. Even after the baby millipedes hatch from their eggs, they may be carried for a varying period, protected by their mother.

Medical Disorders

While no specific diseases are known to be common in millipedes, the author has found rhabidiform nematodes, morphologically indistinguishable from *Strongyloides stercoralis*, in the feces of healthy animals. A variety of different protozoa also have been observed in the fresh stool pellets from these creatures.

4

Insects

METAMORPHOSIS

Higher insects such as moths and butterflies, flies, bees and wasps, and beetles complete a complex series of changes as development proceeds from egg to adult. This transformation includes distinctive changes in structure, size, feeding habits, behavior, and other forms and functions that result in the sexually mature adult. These alterations in physical shape and biological behavior are called *complete metamorphosis*. Each of the continuing stages proceeds after the egg hatches into a larva. Usually the larval insect, which is called a caterpillar or grub, depending upon the family to which it belongs, feeds voraciously and grows quickly. Several molts or *ecdyses* are completed during this rapid growth. Each molt occurs at a different and distinct developmental stage; each stage is separated by another molt. These molts are termed *stadia*, and the form of the larval insect during each stadium is called an *instar*. The only insects that do not undergo some degree of metamorphosis are the primitive bristle-tails, "silver fish," and their relatives (Lapage 1959).

In those species with complete metamorphosis, the larval instars eventually develop into a *pupa* or *chrysalis*, inside of which the adult or *imago* form matures. Often this pupal stage overwinters until warmer spring weather arrives, at which time the sexually adult imago emerges. This system assures the continuation of the species after each successive year's adults perish in autumn.

37

When the structural and dietary habit transformation from egg to adult is more gradual and is not characterized by a grub-like larval form but, rather, a wingless young that otherwise resembles its parents, the process is called *incomplete metamorphosis*. With this form of development, the egg hatches into a *nymph* which grows, molts its cuticle several times, and eventually becomes a sexually mature imago. Examples of this type of development are locusts and grasshoppers, praying mantises, and cockroaches. In these insects, the overwintering form is the egg; usually the imagos die after mating, egg production, and oviposition.

PRAYING MANTISES

"Among the myrtles the mantises moved, lightly, carefully swaying slightly, the quintessence of evil. They were lank and green, with chinless faces and monstrous globular eyes, frosty gold, with an expression of intense, predatory madness in them. The crooked arms, with their fringes of sharp teeth, would be raised in mock supplication to the insect world, so humble, so fervent, trembling slightly when a butterfly flew too close."

Gerald Durrell (1925–   )
MY FAMILY AND OTHER ANIMALS
Copyright 1956

Fig. 32a, page 52

Fig. 32b, page 52

Fig. 32c, page 101

Fig. 32d, page 101

Characterized by graceful movements, fascinating natural habits, impressive size, brightly colored emerald green or bronze bodies, irridescent Tiffany glass wing covers, ever watchful compound eyes, and highly modified curiously reverently folded front limbs that seem like hands lifted in prayer, the common praying mantis, *Mantis religiosa*, has attracted intense scientific interest (**Figures 32a & b**). Some tropical species have evolved remarkable leaf-like adornments on their bodies which very effectively camouflage them (**Figures 32c & d**). Unless they draw attention to themselves by making sudden movements, they are difficult to discern from the surrounding foliage.

The word "mantis" in Greek means "soothsayer" or prophet, and these spectacular insects also have acquired such descriptive names as "Mule-killer" and

"Devil's Horse" in the southern United States where some farmers believe that mantis secretions can kill livestock. According to Italian folk literature, illness can be caused by its stare. In spite of the wealth of folklore and poetic description, the mantis not only is harmless to man, but is beneficial in that it performs a most useful function in helping rid our environment of harmful insects. Durrell's "quintessence of evil" may truly be the quintessence of good.

Mantises have long been one of the most popular and appropriate subjects for insect zoos, elementary school "show and tell" sessions, biology class observations, high school science fair projects, and comparative behavior and neurology experiments.

A member of the insect order, Orthoptera, the mantis undergoes a form of incomplete metamorphosis as it matures. Hatched as a tiny wingless green nymph, it periodically sheds its outgrown exoskeleton and eventually develops wings and wing covers just before it becomes sexually mature. Even newly hatched mantises possess the characteristic elongated and spiky uppermost leg segments, or *coxae* of the first pair of limbs with which it catches its prey in a trap-like manner.

Although other insects are its primary food, larger mantis species can capture and eat small vertebrates such as tree frogs, lizards and even young birds.

The beneficent praying mantis can be observed and, if necessary, caught in the gardens of many North American homes and parks in the spring and summer months. They also may be obtained from nursery suppliers, where they are sold for biological control of insect pests. Egg masses, which typically contain dozens of elongated eggs or developing nymphs, cost about $2.50. When exposed to warm spring temperatures of 21 to 28 °C (69.8 to 82.4 °F), they will hatch out in several weeks. Immediately after hatching, the infant mantises resemble their parents but are much smaller and lack wings. Newly hatched mantises are tolerant of each other; but within a very few days, if they are afforded the opportunity, they will cannibalize their siblings. A similar situation exists with newly hatched spiderlets and scorpions of several species.

Because most chemical insecticides are nonselective and will often destroy beneficial insects and arachnids as well as harmful species, the use of predatory insects such as mantises, parasitic wasps and ladybird beetles for integrated pest control has become increasingly popular during the past two decades.

Housing

Praying mantises should be housed separately, unless they are being mated. Glass or plastic terraria or large glass jars should be fitted with screened tops to prevent the escape of both the mantises and their insect prey. Depending upon their size, some mantises may be kept in cages made from metal hardware cloth that has a mesh size too small to allow escape. These wire cages should be furnished with foliage or sticks upon which the mantis can climb and pursue its prey.

Nutrition

Fig. 33, page 101

A small piece of raw meat placed in the cage will attract flies and other carrion-feeding insects that can enter through the mesh and reach the bait. The mantis merely has to stalk and attack the flies as they enter the cage. Alternatively, grasshoppers, katydids, crickets and moths may be offered as food (**Figure 33**). Smaller mantises may be fed proportionately smaller insects, from tiny newly hatched silk moth larvae or fruit flies to houseflies. Genetically wingless fruit flies, *Drosophila melanogaster*, are particularly valuable as food for very small mantises. They are available from biological supply houses and from college genetics or biology departments. Instructions for culture of these prey species are provided later in this book. As the young mantises grow, they are fed ever larger insect prey. Moths can be caught easily at night when they are attracted to blue electric light bulbs. Any surplus insects may be stored for a day or two in a refrigerator.

Often the insect prey substantially outweighs the stealthy predator. The average time necessary for an adult mantis to strike, grasp an insect, and bring it into contact with its jaws is an efficient 0.29–0.40 seconds. During this very brief time, the spike-studded forelimbs must open and then immediately close upon the prey and bring it into a position where it can be torn apart piecemeal by the mantis's jaws. The accuracy (and, thus, the success rate) of these strikes is in excess of 80 percent; this is far greater than that of a rattlesnake, which may be approximately 25 percent. Only the prey's wings and limb parts are discarded during the eating process. Digestion is rapid, requiring less than 36 hours.

Water

A daily misting of the foliage within the cage is sufficient to meet the requirement for additional moisture of captive mantises. Most of their fluid intake is obtained from the soft body parts of the insect prey upon which they feed.

Reproduction

The sexual dimorphism displayed by mantises is striking. The adult female usually is more heavy bodied and has shorter wings and antennae than the male as was ilustrated in Figures 32a–c. The adult coloration runs from brown to copper, although an occasional bright green individual may be found. In some species, the sexually mature females develop bright lavender eyes (**Figure 34**). In contrast, the male is smaller and possesses a more delicate body shape. The male's wings and antennae are much longer than the female's and his eyes are usually green. In some species the sexually mature male is a metallic blue-green color.

The mating strategy of the praying mantis is truly remarkable. Responding to scents and pheromones given out by the sexually responsive female, the male "homes in" on the female from considerable distances. If he is very quick, agile and above all, lucky, he will mount the female in a male superior fashion (**Figure 35a & b**), though the insects may be hanging upside-down from a branch or twig; unscathed, he then leaves his sluggish mate. This is only one of the

Fig. 34, page 101

Fig. 35a, page 101

Fig. 35b, page 101

Fig. 36a, page 102

Fig. 36b, page 102

Fig. 37a, page 102

Figure 37b. Within a few days, the fertilized female begins to construct one or more bread loaf shaped foam nests into which she deposits about three dozen elongated eggs. The foam soon hardens into a firm insulating material that will protect the undeveloped eggs during the winter. After forming these nests and depositing her eggs, the female mantis dies. The foam nest can be fastened on tree branches and house walls.

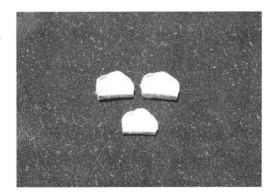

Figure 37c. An old foam nest has been cut to display the many brood chambers, each holding its own egg.

main mating strategies employed by these insects. In at least one species of mantis, the male carries a captured prey insect to his intended mate, feeds it to her to assuage her appetite, and then safely mates with his now-sated bride! In another scenario, the female observes the male's stealthy approach and, at an opportune moment, seizes her erstwhile mate in her modified front legs and immediately **CHEWS OFF HIS HEAD AND ANTERIOR NECK! (Figures 36a & b)**. Although this most dramatic means of mating has been amply documented, by no means is it a foregone conclusion that every male mantis will forfeit its head in payment for his future paternity. Some entomologists have suggested that this behavior is merely an artifact of captivity; however, I have witnessed and photographed mate-eating by completely wild mantises in my garden in Davis, California. In each instance, the female was well fed prior to the attack. Perhaps some species of mantis practice this precopulatory behavior more than others. Whatever the cause, Nature has evolved this strategy for a purpose: within the male mantis's anterior neck is a nerve-rich structure, the subesophageal ganglion. This neural organ exerts a powerful inhibitory influence upon the mating reflex process. When the organ and the inhibition are removed, the male commences abdominal thrusting and sex organ intromission into the genital opening of the female, who by now is quiescent. Laboratory experiments have shown that this behavior can be induced by snipping off the head and anterior neck segments of a male mantis; immediately thereafter, he will circle and attempt to mount—and mate—any appropriately shaped object such as a pencil or stick brought into his now-visionless proximity. An unmated male mantis may live more than a week after his head has been removed, all the while questing in vain for a sexual partner. After mating, the female calmly disengages herself from her now-spent mate and consumes what is left of him after his labors.

Several weeks later, the mated female constructs a foam nest using fluid secreted by auxiliary glandular structures adjacent to her ovipositor (**Figure 37a**). Next, she deposits her many elongated eggs, each in its own chamber (**Figures 37b & c**). The foamy nest material soon hardens into a paper-like material. The fertilized eggs overwinter in the weather-resistant protective nest and complete their development in the early spring months as the weather warms (**Figure 38**). The female dies soon after laying her eggs.

Praying mantises progress from egg to adult by concluding an incomplete metamorphosis; the juveniles grow ever larger and periodically molt their outgrown chitinous exoskeletons as their body size enlarges. With each molt, the young mantises assume more of the adult morphology and eventually mature into winged adults, ready to mate and meet their responsibilities to the continuum of existence in the Earth's faunal inventory.

PHASMATID STICK AND PHYLLIITID LEAF INSECTS

Although far more diverse and common in the tropics, there are several species of Phasmatid stick insects native to temperate North America. Looking like portions of the bare vegetation upon which they live, they are a remarkable example of camouflage (**Figure 39a**). Similarly, the closely related Phylliitid leaf insects of the tropical rain forests bear a striking resemblance to living leaves and twigs (**Figures 39b & c**). Not only are their legs modified by flattened leaf-like appendages and adornments, but thorny spikes and plant-mimicking coloration add to the overall effect of concealment. These interesting creatures are so well camouflaged that they almost completely blend in with their surroundings. Resembling the sticks or leafy twigs upon which they rest, they usually go unnoticed by predators and humans—unless they are betrayed by their slow and deliberate movements.

Stick and leaf insects undergo an incomplete metamorphosis with similar stages to those observed in praying mantises before they reach sexual maturity. The female stick and leaf insects possess only vestigial wings and are substantially larger and heavier bodied than males of the same species. Because they are not beneficial to agriculture, these insects are not commercially available and must be obtained in the wild

Fig. 38, page 102

Fig. 39a, page 102

Fig. 39b, page 102

Fig. 39c, page 103

or from captive bred stock. They rarely live more than eight to twelve months, but are excellent insects to study if one wishes to observe the effects of protective mimicry and camouflage (**Figure 39c**). Generally, females live considerably longer than males.

The larger stick and leaf insects can be handled safely, but care must be taken to avoid being injured by the sharp thorn-like spines that project from the rear limbs and abdomen of some of the larger adult females. Fingers and hands can be protected with leather gloves.

Housing

Stick and leaf insects are exhibited to their best advantage in glass or plastic terraria, or screened cages furnished with the foliage upon which the animals were found in the field. More than one may be housed in the same cage. Like many other insects, the phasmatid stick and phylliitid leaf insects live but a single season. These animals thrive at moderate temperatures, and will become stressed if subjected to extremely cool or warm temperatures.

Water

Most of the moisture obtained by the stick and leaf insects comes from the juices contained in the plants upon which they feed. A light misting of the plants within the terrarium once or twice weekly will provide ample extra moisture.

Nutrition

Ideally, stick and leaf insects should be fed the same vegetation or foliage upon which they were found when captured. If this is impractical, many will eat a variety of other plants. These spectacular insects usually will eat wandering Jew, (*Zebrina pendula*), blackberry, raspberry, and mulberry leaves, romaine lettuce, collard, kale, turnip leaves, etc. Some are more finicky, and several different types of leafy vegetables may have to be offered before finding one that will be accepted.

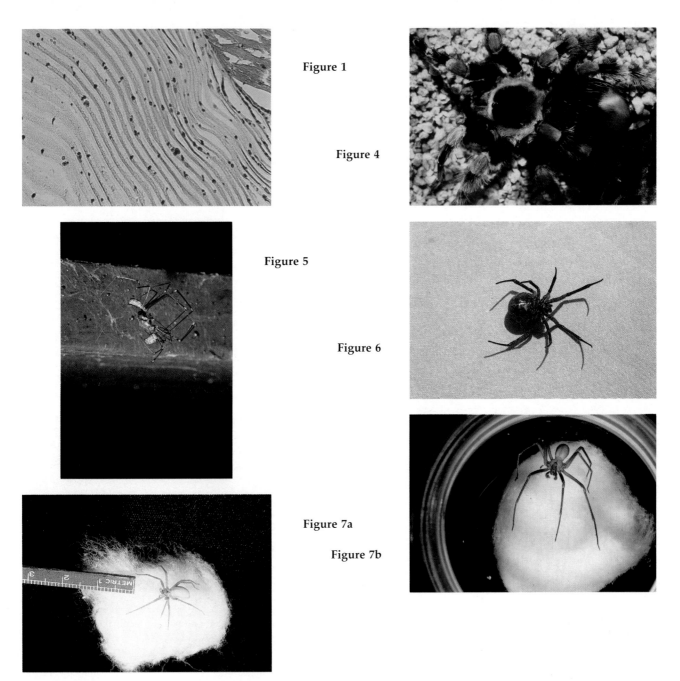

Figure 1. Highly magnified photomicrograph of a stained histologic section of a book lung from a black widow spider. Oxygen and carbon dioxide are exchanged across these page-like "leaves" or lamina.

Figure 4. A female tropical South American red-kneed tarantula, *Brachypelma smithi*. These were often sold in pet shops and, if handled gently, are docile and easily kept in terraria. Note the focal pink hairless area on the opisthosoma, where the animal has flicked off its stiff bristle-like urticarial hairs as a defense against being disturbed.

Figure 5. Although most spiders are solitary creatures except during courtship and mating, others are more gregarious and will even cooperate in the capture and consumption of prey insects. Here two house spiders share a meal of a fly.

Figure 6. A gravid adult female western black widow spider, *Latrodectus mactans hesperus*, from the Mojave Desert of southern California. Note the characteristic crimson hourglass-like figure on the underside by which these venomous spiders can be identified. Most of the volume of the swollen abdomen-like opisthosoma is occupied by ovarian tissue and myriad numbers of yolk-rich eggs.

Figure 7a. A mature female brown recluse or "violin" spider, *Loxosceles reclusa*, a species that is rapidly spreading throughout much of North America. Note the characteristic violin-like marking on the dorsal prosoma, from which this spider gets its common name. This marking is present in both sexes.

Figure 7b. A mature male brown recluse spider. The large pedipalps can be seen easily in this male.

45

Figure 8a.

Figure 8b.

Figure 9

Figure 10d.

Figure 11a

Figure 12a

Figure 8a. A large adult female garden spider tending her web.

Figure 8b. An adult male garden spider. Smaller than the female, note the slimmer opisthosoma, and bulbous pedipalps.

Figure 9. "Daisies tell." Note how well the crab spider sitting in the center of this yellow blossom is camouflaged. With its protective coloration, the spider merely has to await the arrival of unwary flying insects to obtain its meals. Like jumping spiders, these spiders possess excellent vision.

Figure 10d. Here a trapdoor spider leaves her camouflaged nest. The trapdoor closes after she exits. Upon her return, she will pry open the lid and enter. Copyright 1933, Lee Passmore and the National Geographic Society.

Figure 11a. A mygalomorph spider, *Theraphosa leblondi*, drinking from a Petri dish. These large spiders can drink a surprising volume of water.

Figure 12a. As soon as an insect has blundered into a web, it is immediately enwrapped in silken threads into a cocoon-like package ready to have its body fluids consumed.

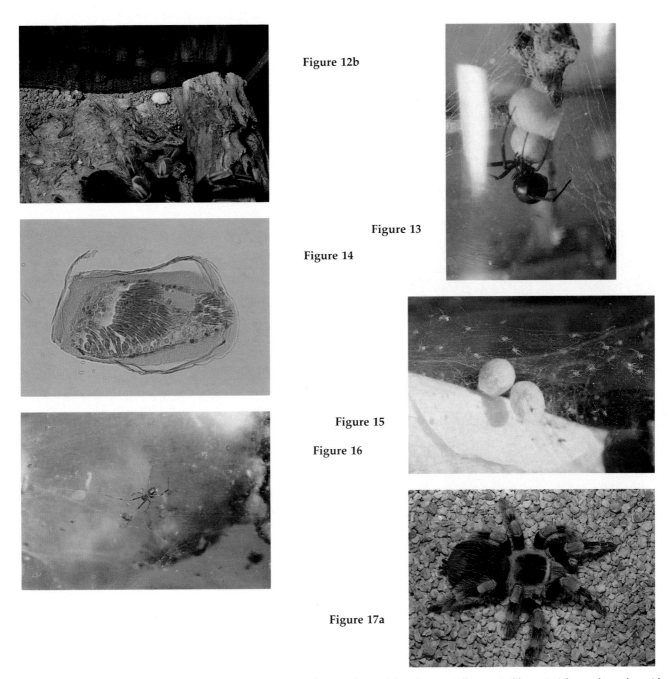

Figure 12b

Figure 13

Figure 14

Figure 15

Figure 16

Figure 17a

Figure 12b. The major excretory waste of arachnids is guanine, deposited as a white microcrystalline paste-like material, seen here alongside the glass wall of the terrarium.

Figure 13. The mated female black widow spider constructs several tough silken egg cases into which she deposits several dozen fertilized eggs. These spiders are quite attentive to their egg cases and not only defend them against intruders, but also assist in the emergence of the newly hatched spiderlets. See Figure 15.

Figure 14. A greatly magnified stained histological section of a single black widow spider embryo at an early stage of development.

Figure 15. As soon as she detects movements within an egg case, the female creates a small opening through which the tiny spiders escape. At first, they are tolerant of each other, but soon begin to cannibalize each other.

Figure 16. A sexually mature male black widow spider can be indentified easily by its greatly enlarged pedipalps which are employed in sperm transfer.

Figure 17a. The same spider shown in Figure 4 approximately 3 weeks after the preceeding photograph was obtained. Note the now dark hairless area. Less than 24 hours after this exposure was made, the spider shed its old exoskeleton.

Figure 17b

Figure 17c

Figure 18

Figure 19a

Figure 19b

Figure 20a

Figure 17b. Photograph made immediately after this spider molted. Note the oval carapace-like covering that once formed the upper surface of the prosoma, or "cephalothorax," in the upper right. The balance of the shed exoskeleton is shown in the lower center. The freshly molted spider is in the center has regenerated her urticarial hairs on her opisthosoma.

Figure 17c. A freshly molted exoskeleton of a goliath spider, *Theraphosa leblondi*. Note the openings into the walking legs. pedipalps, and the second pair of book lungs; and the remnant of the sucking stomach.

Figure 18. Looking outward from the shed carapace through the eight eye-like ocelli. It is doubtful whether these creatures possess visual acuity. They probably form light and dark shadow-like ocular stimuli, rather than precise images and must rely on tactile senses to detect their prey and explore their immediate environment.

Figure 19a. Occasionally, a well-meaning, but uninformed, person will accidentally dismember a pet in an attempt to assist it in its shedding process. Here a mygalomorph lies dismembered after such a traumatic event.

Figure 19b. A rose-hair tarantula after having been attacked by a large scorpion. Two of the walking legs on the right side have been lost. Note the haemolymph oozing from the sites of trauma.

Figure 20a. A predatory wasp, *Pepsis*, often called a "tarantula hawk" because of its habit of stinging a tarantula and depositing one or more eggs onto its immobilized prey. After hatching, the wasp's larvae feed upon the living, but paralyzed, spider, eventually killing it.

48

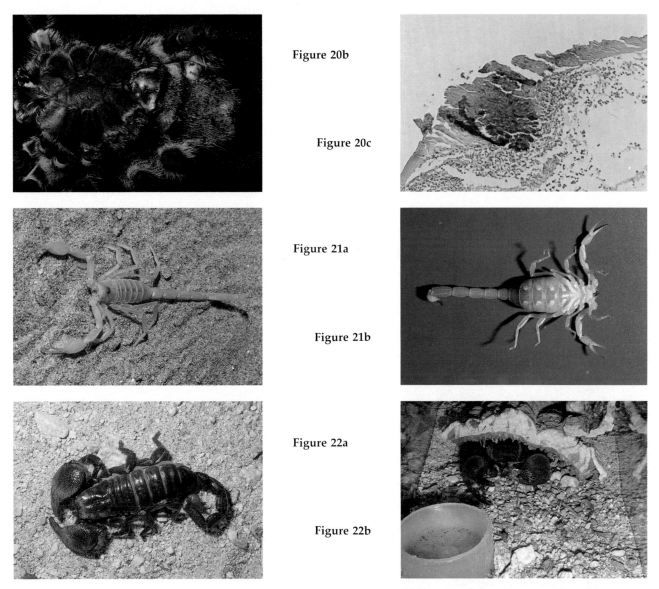

Figure 20b

Figure 20c

Figure 21a

Figure 21b

Figure 22a

Figure 22b

Figure 20b. An invasive growth that appeared to arise from the opening of the third left book lung in a Mexican red-kneed tarantula.

Figure 20c. Histological section of the mass. The abundant golden brown pigment is believed to be melanin or melanin-like and was found to have displaced some of the internal organs. H & E stain, X 27.

Figure 21a. A mature female hairy scorpion, *Hadrurus hirsutus*, from the southwestern Mojave desert. Like most arachnids, scorpions have four pair of walking legs and a pair of highly specialized pedipalps. In the case of the scorpions, the pedipalps are pincer-like organs that are employed in grasping prey and during courtship ritual "dances." Scorpions also possess a segmented tail-like metasoma that bears a bulbous telson and recurved sting at its end. Paired venom glands and muscles fill much of the telson and aid in expressing the venom through the sting.

Figure 21b. Similar scorpion as illustrated in Figure 21a. In order to obtain this photograph of the ventral structures of the animal, she was anesthetized briefly with a volatile anesthetic. Note the eight openings to the book lungs and the paired comb-like pectines adjacent to the fourth pair of walking legs. These organs are thought to be sensitive to vibrations and scent-rich prey insects and spiders.

Figure 22a. A large adult Egyptian emperor scorpion, *Pandinus imperator*. These impressive arachnids possess well-developed and powerful pincer-like chelate pedipalps that almost rival the claws of a crayfish or small lobster.

Figure 22b. The massive pedipalps are used to grasp and manipulate the prey as it is torn apart by the celicerae, and swallowed.

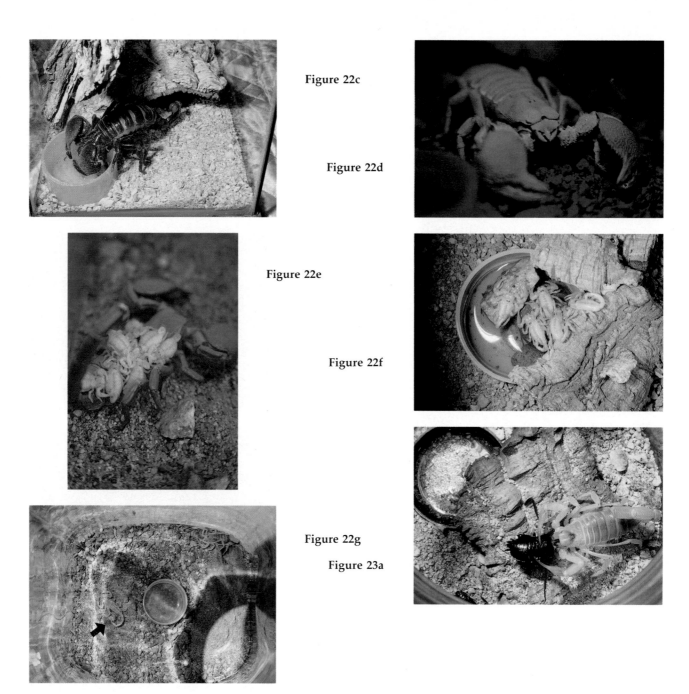

Figure 22c. An emperor scorpion drinking from a shallow vessel.

Figure 22d–e. When illuminated with ultraviolet light, scorpions display a vivid fluorescence. The dark pigment and fluorescence develops only after one or more exoskeletal molts.

Figure 22f. Four one-month-old emperor scorpions immediately after they left their mother's back. Here they congregate around a water container in which stones have been placed to permit the baby scorpions to crawl to safety should they topple in.

Figure 22g. Scorpions molt their exoskeletons in a fashion much like spiders. Here a hairy desert scorpion (upper right) and its shed cuticle (left center).

Figure 23a. Contrary to popular belief, some scorpions not only drain the body fluids and soft body parts of their prey, but actually swallow almost the entire victim. Here a hairy scorpion is seen devouring a large cockroach. After the huge meal, only a few small remnants of the cockroach's legs were left behind and the scorpion was left much swollen.

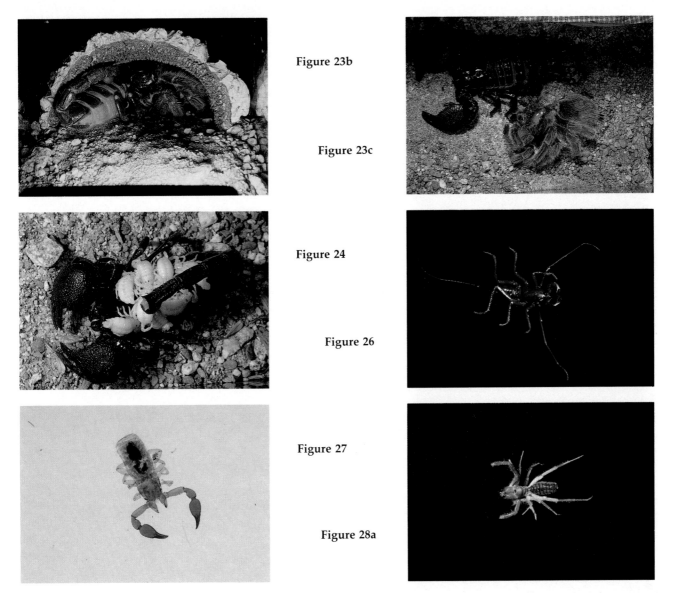

Figure 23b

Figure 23c

Figure 24

Figure 26

Figure 27

Figure 28a

Figure 23b. An emperor scorpion with a paritally consumed rose-hair tarantula, *Grammostola spathulata*, that had died one day prior to it being offered to the scorpion. This was an unusual occurrence because scorpions prefer to consume prey whom they have subdued.

Figure 23c. The remains of the meal approximately 18 hours after the photograph for Figure 23b was made. Note the partially liquified contents of the dead spider and the expansion of the scorpion's body.

Figure 24. Scorpions give birth to fully formed living young rather than depositing immature eggs that must incubate in the environment. The young scorpions ride upon the back of their mother for one or more weeks and depend on her protection.

Figure 26. A whip scorpion or "vinegaroon." Note the long, segmented, antenna-like metasoma, or "tail," and the well developed pincer-like pedipalps with which these animals grasp their prey. These arachnids lack a venomous sting.

Figure 27. Pseudoscorpion. Although most pseudoscorpions are miniscule creatures measuring only a few millimeters in length, some species grow much larger. They lack a tail-like metasoma. They are harmless to humans. Some of the smaller species live in forest litter; others live in libraries where they subsist on tiny insects and mites that infest books.

Figure 28a. Less well known than the true spiders and scorpions, the solifugid "wind," "sun," and "camel" spiders are not true spiders, but are placed in a class by themselves. Note the four pairs of walking legs, the robust and blunt-tipped pedipalps, the massive jaws and the segmented opisthosoma which is formed from joined plates on back and belly. Although these creatures lack venom, their huge jaws can deliver a fatal crushing bite to their prey.

Figure 28b

Figure 31a

Figure 31b

Figure 31c

Figure 32a

Figure 32b

Figure 28b. Less well known than the true spiders and scorpions, the solifugid "wind," "sun," and "camel" spiders are not true spiders, but are placed in a class by themselves. Note the four pairs of walking legs, the robust and blunt-tipped pedipalps, the massive jaws and the segmented opisthosoma which is formed from joined plates on back and belly. Although these creatures lack venom, their huge jaws can deliver a fatal crushing bite to their prey.

Figure 31a–c. Millipedes have become popular animals for woodland terraria. They are harmless to humans and easy to care for, preferring a diet of vegetables and fruit. Members of the same species may differ markedly in coloration.

Figures 32a & b. Praying mantises. The female shown in Figure 32a is stouter bodied and has shorter antennae and wings while the male illustrated in Figure 32b possesses a more slender body, long antennae and wings and tends to be more brilliantly colored.

52

Reproduction

Many, if not most, native stick insects appear to employ parthenogenesis in reproduction, much like the common aphids; in some species, males are virtually unknown. Females produce eggs which contain female embyros.

However, phylliitid leaf insects are either male or female and internal fertilization is employed. Tropical leaf insects reproduce readily in captivity and are easy to care for. The fertile shiny, dark, and nearly spherical eggs (**Figure 39b**) are merely dropped onto leaves or the ground at random and are left to overwinter *in situ*. Incubation time is temperature-dependent; it ranges between a few days to several weeks. The juveniles are much the same as the adults in morphology, but lack wings. Their growth is rapid, and after several molts they develop wings and reach sexual maturity. The wings of females are greatly reduced and do not permit flight; those of males are functional. It is likely that females produce a sex-attractant pheromone to which males are irresistibly drawn, in a similar fashion to that of praying mantises.

Fig. 39b, page 102

Medical Disorders

There appear to be no specific diseases common to these insects, but *Bacillus thuringiensis* can infect them and cause disease and death. An overly moist or filthy cage environment must be avoided.

TOMATO HORNWORMS (SPHINX MOTH LARVAE)

The scourge of most home vegetable gardeners, the tomato hornworm is the larval form of the impressive sphinx moth, one of the heaviest bodied moths living in temperate life zones. Similar in shape, life cycle, and habits is the tobacco hornworm, which is the larval form of the hawkmoth. For purposes of brevity and because tomato plants are grown by more people than tobacco, only the sphinx moth larvae and tomato hornworms will be discussed. These large insects are particularly valuable for classroom teaching because they can so easily be fed year-around on a diet of tomato leaves which can be grown under conditions of artificial illumination. Because of their high content of toxic plant juices, these insects are not suitable for prey for insectivores.

As anyone who has grown tomato plants without the application of pesticides knows, each summer is marked by the appearance of enormous green grubs, bearing a horn-like spur on one end, that can defoliate tomato plants very rapidly. These larvae often exceed 6 cm (2+ inches) in length and weigh well over 15 grams (a half ounce). Although birds such as young blue jays and shrikes will attack and eat them, older, more experienced birds ignore them entirely, or may pick at them as if to entertain themselves, but appear to find them distasteful to eat.

Because sphinx moths are widely distributed throughout much of North America, tomato hornworms are readily available each summer. The greatest advantage to keeping tomato hornworms under study is that they are easily fed and, because of their large size and camouflaged coloration, are very useful in the classroom for teaching both complete metamorphosis and the survival benefits of cryptic color and pattern in the insect world. They can be found on vigorously growing tomato plants by carefully searching for cleanly eaten tomato leaves with only the central leaf vein remaining, and large black fecal pellets shaped like spools that may litter the base of the plant. Once found, the larvae can be plucked gently from the plant and carried home or to the classroom. Although their spiky horn looks formidable, these larvae are not harmful if picked up with bare hands. They may regurgitate some plant juice onto the plucker's fingers, but this can be removed easily with soap and water.

Housing

The most simple means for keeping tomato hornworms during their actively growing period of development is to place them on potted living tomato plants. Depending upon the number and size of larvae to be kept under observation, one should anticipate having to grow several tomato plants so that they can be rotated, giving each an opportunity to recover from the voracious depredations of these always hungry grubs before again being used as a picnic ground. As long as enough tomato leaves are provided, the sphinx moth larvae will not attempt to leave the plant upon which they are dining. Once the larvae are ready to enter the next stage of their development, they cease eating and migrate to the soil at the bottom of the plant, burrow into the earth, and form their pupal cases that are characterized by the prominent recurved hook-like projection at one end of the dark brown chrysalis. Where the winter seasonal temperature falls below 10 °C (50 °F), the pupae overwinter and shortly after the weather warms the following spring the moths emerge.

If adult sphinx moths are to be kept for brief periods, a screened cage should be provided. Because of the large size of these insects, the sides of the cage should be covered with 1/4-inch mesh hardware cloth that will confine the moths, yet permit observation.

Nutrition

These insects are nearly exclusive in their preference for tomato leaves and immature green tomatoes. Tomato plants may be grown from seeds or purchased as young seedlings from nursery dealers. The growing plants should be cared for as they would be if they were being grown to feed humans and will require regular watering and the application of fertilizer. If enough plants are grown and rotated among the developing hornworm larvae, there is no reason they should not produce tomatoes for the family's consumption. An adequate amount of suitable light must be provided for the tomato plants to conduct photosynthesis.

The adult sphinx moths subsist on plant nectar that they siphon with their proboscis, which is kept tightly coiled like a watch spring when it is not deployed. When used to imbibe nectar, this tubular organ is straightened, and extended and inserted deeply into the flowers. In captivity, these large adult moths can be fed a dilute solution of honey or Karo syrup and water.

Artifical diets for sphinx moth (tomato horn-worms) and silk moth larvae are available from:

Bio-Serve
P.O. Box 450
Frenchtown, N.J. 08825
1-800-473-2155

Water

Although actively feeding larvae may imbibe small volumes of free water from the leaves upon which they are living, they receive most of their needed moisture from the tender tomato foliage and young fruits.

Medical Disorders

Like some other insects, sphinx moth larvae are susceptible to infection by the bacterial pathogen *Bacillus thuringiensis*. As long as otherwise healthy larvae are actively feeding on tomato plants and are not dusted or sprayed with insecticides containing *Bacillus thuringiensis*, infection is rare.

Some parasitic wasps, particularly *Apanteles congregatus*, utilize sphinx moth larvae as prey upon which their own developing larvae feed, but there is only a minor risk of predation in captive hornworms kept for indoor observation.

STAG, RHINOCEROS, AND ELEPHANT BEETLES

Most of the world's insect zoos try to have on display some examples of the impressive European stag beetles, *Lucanus cervus*, and the North American species, *L. elephas*, because the males possess enormously outsized mandibles with which they joust and wrestle other males during their courtship battles. Even larger beetles such as the South American stag beetles, *Chiasognathus grantii*, and the Asian *Cladognathus giraffe* possess still longer and more highly developed mandibles. The gargantuan tropical rhinoceros beetles have always been enormously popular exhibits wherever they are displayed. Some of these impressive insects measure nearly 15 cm (6 inches) in length (**Figure 40**).

Fig. 40, page 103

Housing

These huge insects are inhabitants of the forest floor where they walk slowly in search of food or mates. They thrive in humid, yet well-ventilated, terraria furnished with well-composted forest litter. This humus should be distributed over a porous rock and sand base so that any excessive moisture will be permitted to drain. Large pieces of cork oak bark or similar nonresinous wood should be provided as refuges. A few hardy houseplants such as Dracaena, Hibiscus, or broad-leaf bromeliads can be planted in the terrarium for decoration. These beetles are not particularly agile climbers, and a lid made with metal hardware cloth will confine them nicely. Because these insects will enter combat with each other if overcrowded, only one or two of them should be housed together unless the cage is large and provided with many hiding places into which the beetles can retire. Inverted and halved coconut shells with one edge chipped out serve well as beetle "igloos."

Water Provision

Although they receive the bulk of their dietary water from the moisture content of their varied diet of tropical fruit, they will, from time to time, imbibe water from shallow vessels or leaf hollows such as those that are found in living bromeliad plants and other epiphytes.

Nutrition

Most of these forest-dwelling gigantic beetles are opportunistic generalized feeders, dining upon whatever they encounter in their daily travels. In captivity, they will thrive on a diet of tropical fruit such as papaya, banana, mango, etc. with an occasional meal of commercial canned dog or cat food and grated carrots or apple. If the cost of fresh tropical fruit is too burdensome, applesauce, chopped pear, peach, and apricot prepared as for human infant feeding can be substituted. Fresh containers of food should be provided at 24-to 48-hour intervals, and only enough food should be placed in the cage as will be consumed within a period of 24 hours. This will help prevent food spoilage and the accumulation of bacterial and fungal pathogens.

Reproduction

These insects must go through a complete metamorphosis before achieving adulthood. After mating, the female deposits her eggs in decomposed pulpy wood. These eggs hatch into grub-like larvae that spend many months burrowing into and devouring wood and forest debris, fallen fruit, and carrion. With time, the larvae excavate shallow burrows in which they pupate and eventually emerge as fully formed beetles. After mating and depositing their eggs, the adults usually die, but some have survived over two years.

Many of these insects are collected from the wild or grown specifically to be killed and mounted in shadow-box glazed frames to be used as curios. Currently, these mounted beetles sell for approximately $35 each, with exceptionally large specimens commanding a price of about $60.

EXOTIC COCKROACHES

procrastination is the
art of keeping
up with yesterday

(quoted by Archy, the cockroach who was unable to use the shift key on the typewriter for capitals and punctuation)

Donald Robert Perry Marquis
1878–1937

To the vast majority of people, cockroaches are foul and loathesome vermin created solely to blight one's existence. Amazingly, there are insect collections that display not only the more cosmopolitan forms of cockroaches that infest homes and businesses in North America and Europe, but such creatures as the wingless giant hissing cockroach (**Figure 41**) from tropical habitats and several other species that approach a length of 7.5 cm (3 inches)! The winged *Blaberus gigantea* are equally as large (**Figure 42a & b**). Having seen some of these beasties in the wild and in insect zoo collections, I am no longer amazed at how much interest the viewers exhibit when first exposed to a roach nearly the size of a house mouse. Some of these huge cockroaches live for more than two years under captive conditions, but most live less than a year. Most exhibits include sufficient animals to display several nymphal stages as well as adults.

Fig. 41, page 103

Fig. 42a, page 103

Fig. 42b, page 103

Housing

Most cockroaches are tolerant of a wide variation in their captive habitats and will thrive as long as they are not overcrowded, are provided with adequate hiding areas or refuges, and are not kept in a too-moist cage.

Because these insects can establish themselves easily in such a variety of living conditions, their cages must be escape-proof. The *former* owner of one or more giant cockroaches is not going to be especially welcomed by the neighbors if these "pets" escape and set up housekeeping elsewhere in the adjoining dwellings!

Nutrition

Being not too particular in their dietary preferences, tropical cockroaches will eagerly accept a broad variety of fruits, commercial dry kibbled dog or cat food, and table scraps. Only enough food should be placed in their cage to feed them for a day or two because it may spoil and attract vermin and foster bacterial or fungal growth. These insects will resort to cannibalism if sufficient food is not available.

Water

Like their smaller cousins infesting many large cities, the tropical cockroaches are attracted to moisture and will drink water furnished in shallow containers. If a small piece of clean cellulose sponge is placed into the container, the cockroaches may find it easier to imbibe the water, but it is important to change the water and rinse the sponge daily.

Reproduction

Cockroaches go through an incomplete metamorphosis before reaching adulthood. As the young insect grows, it periodically molts its old and outgrown epidermis and, with its first adult molt, emerges as a sexually mature creature ready to reproduce and give rise to future generations.

Mated females deposit their fertilized eggs in litter or upon pieces of cardboard or nonresinous tree bark. The eggs are contained in thin-walled golden brown brood capsules from which the nymphal young emerge after a brief incubation that, under warm and humid conditions, may require only a few days, but may be prolonged at cooler and drier environmental conditions.

AQUATIC INSECTS

Many species of aquatic or semiaquatic insects are kept in aquaria or large glass or plastic containers by limnologists and biology teachers. Among the species which can be kept for variable periods of time are diving beetles, *Dytiscus, Hydrophilus, Acilius, Colymbetes*, etc., the giant water bug, *Lethocerus americanus*, water boatmen, whirligig beetles, *Gyrinus*, backswimmers, water striders and dragonfly nymphs. Some, like the great water beetle, *Hydrophilus triangularis*, grow to nearly 4 cm (1.5 inches) in length, and the giant water bug grows to approximately 7 cm (slightly less than 3 inches) and is fearsome predator of anything that it can overcome, including frogs; also, it can deliver a painful bite on the fingers of unwary people.

These aquatic insects are common inhabitants of still ponds, creeks, and rapidly running riverine systems and can be captured easily in long-handled dip or sweep nets. Some of these creatures utilize a complete metamorphosis; others go through an incomplete cycle, marked by the presence of nymphal stages rather than grub-like larvae. The beetles, water boatmen, and backswimmers are fully capable of flight. The dragonfly nymphs will eventually emerge from the water as winged adults and should be released outdoors. Most of these aquatic insects are carnivorous predatory creatures, and several can pursue and capture even the most actively swimming fish. For this reason, these aquatic insects are not suitable for a community fish tank where they could quickly depopulate a collection of small fish, tadpoles, or ornamental snails.

The means by which some of these insects exchange their respiratory gases is interesting. Some carry bubbles of air with them from which they extract oxygen; as the oxygen is depleted, this bubble must be renewed with fresh air that the insect obtains at the water's surface; other aquatic insects such as many of the water beetles are equipped with a "plastron" consisting of a surface of very fine hair-like extensions on their ventral surface upon which a thin layer of air adheres. It is seen when the underside of the beetle is viewed while immersed in water and appears as a bright, silvery, and highly reflective surface (**Figure 43a**).

Fig. 43a, page 103

The swimming legs of many of these aquatic insects are furnished by fringes of short stiff hairs which serve to broaden these limbs into effective organs of propulsion. In others, the rear limbs are greatly elongated oar-like instruments (**Figure 43b**).

Fig. 43b, page 104

Housing

Aquatic beetles and water striders should be kept in fresh water aquarium tanks planted with one or more species of living pond weeds that are rooted securely or otherwise fastened to the bottom gravel. Most do well at room or slightly warmer water temperatures. As with other species mentioned previously, it is important to maintain high water quality by using filter systems, and avoiding overcrowding and overfeeding. An escape-proof cover made of glass, plastic or fine-mesh screen should be fitted to the tank. A small trapdoor in the tank lid will simplify the insertion of food items while lessening the opportunity for escape by the aquarium's inhabitants. An overhead aquarium light will aid in seeing the tank's inhabitants and will also permit vital photosynthesis. Because many of these insects are native to rapidly flowing streams, they prefer a slightly cooler environmental temperature, but will tolerate aquarium tank water as warm as 25.5 °C (78 °F) at a pH of 6.8–7.2. The pH of the water can be determined by using chemical-impregnated test strips or a pH meter.

Nutrition

Since these insects are predatory, they capture other aquatic creatures within their immediate environment. Other invertebrates such as insects, snails, and worms, as well as fish are their diet. Some will consume leftover commercial fish food. Depending upon the nature, number of animals, and the availability of food sources, these animals should be fed once to three times weekly.

Reproduction

Aquatic beetles, like most insects, employ internal fertilization, and the sexes are sometimes different in size (the females usually are larger than the males). Eggs are deposited on aquatic vegetation or in the soil at the margins of the pond or stream to which these insects are native. The eggs overwinter and hatch in the early spring months; when their metamorphosis is completed, winged adults are available to mate and begin another generation.

Medical Disorders

Like some other insects, these aquatic invertebrates are susceptible to infection with *Bacillus thurin-*

giensis, but if the water quality is maintained at a healthy level, infection would be unusual. One thing must be remembered: these insects are carnivorous and some are cannibalistic; if cannibalism occurs, it may be a signal to provide more food. It is only natural for these insects to live relatively brief lives. One way that the longevity of a pond community can be increased is to rotate the insects frequently. Keep the beetles, etc. under observation for a week or two and then release them where they were captured, and replace them with freshly captured specimens. In this way, the natural population is not as severely disturbed as it would be if otherwise healthy animals were not returned to the wild.

5

Crustaceans

TERRESTRIAL AND ARBOREAL HERMIT CRABS

There are three species of creatures who
    when they seem coming are going,
When they seem going they come:
    diplomats, women, and crabs.

John Hay
1838–1905

Pet shops and aquarium shops have been selling a variety of aquatic, terrestrial and arboreal hermit crabs for the past eight to ten years. Prices have remained relatively stable for the common Puerto Rican and Floridian hermit crabs, *Coenobita clypeatus*, (**Figure 44a**) which sell for about $2.50 to $3.00, depending upon the value of the shell in which the crab is residing. Frequently, the shell itself is worth more than the crab, making the beastie an extra dividend. These crustaceans are steadily becoming more popular, particularly as pets for apartment dwellers. They are noiseless, require little care and do not have to be taken on walks on cold rainy nights. Of course, they are neither cuddly nor affectionate, but they are colorful and interesting to watch as they eat, using their oversized main claw to place morsels of food delicately into their mouths. When seeking refuge from their predators or tormentors, they retreat into their borrowed snail shell and close the entrance with their heavily armored claw (**Figure 44b**).

Fig. 44a, page 104

Fig. 44b, page 104

65

Housing

Fig. 44c, page 104

Terrestrial and arboreal hermit crabs are kept most often in a terrarium or similar smooth-sided enclosure furnished with an inclined gravel "beach" leading to an artifical "tide line." A few stout branches of well-weathered drift wood should be propped securely so that the crabs may climb without hazard of falling (**Figure 44c**), but care must be taken to prevent their escape from their terrarium.

Although these crabs are native to the vegetation growing within approximately 25 meters of the high tide line of tropical marine tidal zones, they will tolerate brackish or even fresh water rather well. Once they have matured to their adult form, they need to return to the ocean or estuary only to breed. Their gill filaments are kept moist with residual rain water caught in leaves or abandoned sea shells.

The tree hermit crab grows slowly and, as it outgrows its current snail shell (which is its usual home), it competes with other crabs occupying larger quarters. Failing to successfully dispossess another crab from its resident shell, many crabs will utilize almost any other hollow item: old light bulb sockets, open beer cans, eggs shells, small coconut shells, etc.; all have been found with these curious crabs living within their confines. The crab's abdomen is twisted in a counterclockwise coil to match that of the snail

Fig. 44d, page 104

shells it normally inhabits (**Figure 44d**). Because they can leave their borrowed shells with ease, they should not be housed in bird cages or similar cages from which they can easily escape once they have shrugged out of their mobile abodes.

In captivity, these crabs may live for as long as ten years.

Water

Fig. 45, page 104

A water source easily accessible to the crab must be provided. Shallow natural sea shells (**Figure 45**), ceramic dishes, ash trays, or an artificial "beach" with a downward sloping area offer the crabs an opportunity to enter and leave the water as required. Ideally, the water should be saline, but fresh water is tolerated. Because of the crabs' omnivorous diet and lack of etiquette in dining, the water tends to become fouled with food particles and must be cleaned frequently.

Nutrition

In nature, terrestrial and arboreal hermit crabs forage along the water-gravel or sand margin almost daily, and are omnivorous. In captivity, they will readily accept hard kibbled dog food, pelleted poultry ration, chopped or sliced of apple, table scraps, etc. Most crabs will eat a variety of fruits and vegetables. Only small amounts of food should be offered daily to prevent overfeeding and spoilage of uneaten portions.

Reproduction

Like other marine crustaceans, terrestrial and arboreal hermit crabs must return to the water's edge in order to deposit and fertilize their eggs. They do not employ a complete metamorphosis but, rather, go through a series of juvenile or larval stages as they grow larger; after a final juvenile molt, they become sexually mature adults, ready to continue their species.

Once they have gone through several larval stages and molts, the terrestrial forms can emerge from the water and live ashore.

Medical Disorders

I know of no specific diseases common to these crabs other than an ulcerative shell disorder caused by the chitin-digesting bacterium, *Beneckia chitinovora*. They are probably also susceptible to one or more of the species of *Vibrio* endemic to other crustaceans, such as shrimp and lobsters, but these epidemic diseases usually are not a clinical problem in a solitary animal kept as a pet.

Fig. 46a, page 105

Fig. 46b, page 105

Comment

I would be remiss if I didn't make a cautionary statement: the single large pincer borne by these small crabs **MUST** be respected by the unwary (**Figure 46a & b**). Once fastened upon a fingertip, it almost requires an Act of Congress to induce these crabs to release their grip. The more agitated they become, the harder they pinch. (Novice hermit crab handlers can be differentiated readily from experts by the presence of one or more fresh blood blisters on their fingertips!) A quick dunk in a water bath or beneath running water will usually induce the crab to release its tenacious grip.

AQUATIC CRABS

Fig. 47a, page 105

Fig. 47b, page 105

Fig. 47c, page 105

Constructed along the same pattern, but usually more brightly colored than their terrestrial and arboreal cousins, the wholly aquatic crabs have a similar life cycle except that they spend their entire lives immersed in either salt or brackish water. Their gills act as respiratory organs that extract oxygen from their watery milieu. Some look much like edible crabs (**Figure 47a**); others bear enormous claws on one arm (**Figure 47b**); yet others, like their terrestiral cousins, appropriate vacant shells for their mobile homes (**Figure 47c**).

Housing and Water

Aquatic crabs must be kept in clean water. If the water in their tank is permitted to become foul, the crabs' respiratory functions become impaired and the opportunity for bacterial and fungal growth is greatly enhanced. Aquatic crabs usually are kept in aquaria in which they share the space and resources with ornamental fish. Because it is the nature of many crustaceans to be secretive, some provision for seeking refuge should be made for these creatures; also, some species of fish will continually harass small crabs unless they have some place in which to seek shelter. Half of a clay flower pot or a piece of clay pipe will be a welcome addition to the tank in which crabs are kept. Much of their time between active foraging and exploration of the tank's confines will be spent hiding in the refuge.

Nutrition

Unlike terrestrial and arboreal hermit crabs that often prefer a more varied diet, aquatic crabs eat mostly animal material. It is for this reason that they often are kept as scavengers in community fish tanks. Although they usually dine upon dead fish and uneaten fish food, they are capable of capturing their food—and perhaps your favorite live fish!

Reproduction

Aquatic crabs reproduce similarly to their terrestrial and arboreal kin. Fertilization of mature eggs is external, and the female crab carries her brood of fertilized eggs beneath her tail until they hatch into free-living larvae. After a variable period of development and following several molts, the juvenile crabs finally mature into adults and, if a potential partner of the opposite sex is available, will mate. Larval crabs (following incomplete metamorphosis) resemble their parents, but are sexually immature.

Medical Disorders

Aquatic crabs are susceptible to the same infectious diseases that affect terrestrial and arboreal crustaceans, but are more likely to be exposed to *Vibrio* than are land and tree-dwelling crabs; when they are suspected of being infected, they should be isolated from their healthy contemporaries.

CRAYFISH

'tis the voice of the lobster:
I heard him declare,
"You have baked me brown,
I must sugar my hair."

Lewis Carroll
1832–1898

Fig. 48a, page 105

Caught in the wild for many years and only recently raised under aquacultural conditions for human consumption, the common freshwater crayfish (or crawfish) *Cambarus affinis* (**Figure 48a**), *C. virilis*, *C. clarkii*, and *Astacus nigrescens*, are suitable food for several species of zoo animals as well as humans. The names "crayfish" and "crawfish" are thought to have been derived from the French word, "e' crevisse," which means inhabiting a crevice. These crustaceans will accept a wide variety of food items and will thrive in captivity as long as their water remains clean and cool. Several amphibians and a few snake species are so adapted to a diet of crayfish that they rarely will accept other food items.

Housing

Aquaria fitted with an adequate filtration system and some means for keeping the water cooled to less than 20 °C (68 °F) are appropriate vessels. Although some species are more heat-tolerant than others, most, if not all, prefer cooler water, and it is essential to protect these crustaceans from overly warm water. Well-weathered redwood or oaken troughs or vats have been used to produce small numbers of these miniature lobster-like creatures. If a large volume of these animals is to be produced, a flow-through raceway system may be the most economical means for maintaining high water quality—but it wastes water because no recycling occurs. The pH of the water should be maintained between 6.8 to 7.2. Small volumes of phosphoric acid can be added to lower the pH, and small amounts of calcium carbonate can be used to raise it. Adjust the pH gradually by adding only the minimum amounts of phosphoric acid or calcium carbonate. If municipal tap water or well water is found to exceed the narrow range of the preferred pH, it is advisable to use bottled spring water or distilled water rather than adding large amounts of chemicals.

Pieces of clay pipe or tiles should be placed into the culture tanks to provide refuge. Crayfish are cannibalistic and will attack and kill their own species if they are overcrowded or stressed excessively. When they are deprived of food for more than a day or two, they may dine upon the weakest among their kin; they are particularly prone to cannibalism during their periodic molt. The frequency of molting is determined by the age, growth, and the amount of exterior wear and tear of the chitinous surfaces. After molting, the exoskeleton remains soft for a day or two, and it is during this time that the crayfish are vulnerable to trauma and attack by their peers. During these molts, missing legs, claws, tailflukes and other body parts are replaced. In short, it is best to keep crayfish well fed and uncrowded. Having a place in which to seek solitude and to hide when they are molting their exoskeleton lessens their cannibalistic tendencies. Any surplus crayfish can be consumed by humans; they make excellent "finger food" (**Figure 48b**) and are excellent in seafood dishes.

Fig. 48b, page 106

Nutrition

Crayfish are omnivorous and will consume almost anything edible. Under natural conditions, they are scavengers and, therefore, serve as valuable removers of carrion such as dead fish and other animals.

A captive diet of good-quality canned dog or cat food appears to furnish adequate nutrition. Both ends of the cans should be perforated with a pointed can opener that will produce a series of triangular holes through which the crayfish can winkle out small pieces of food. The attached lids help keep the canned food from being consumed too rapidly or fouling the water. The cans should be left until they are empty, and then removed and replaced with freshly opened cans of food.

Reproduction

Mature females produce clutches of round eggs once or more often yearly. These eggs are fertilized by the sperm of sexually mature males and are carried as adhered masses beneath the tail of the female until they hatch several weeks later. The incubation time depends on the temperature of the water in which these animals are kept.

Like crabs, crayfish do *not* go through a complete metamorphosis. The young look much like their parents, but are considerably smaller. They feed upon whatever edible detritus they find in their aquatic environment. Under most conditions of culture at cool temperatures, crayfish mature to adults in their second or third year. Some warm water tolerant species may achieve sexual maturity late in their first year.

Medical Conditions

If they are kept in a clean, uncrowded, and cool water environment, crayfish usually remain healthy. Like their aquatic crab cousins, crayfish are susceptible to bacterial infections with *Beneckia chitinovora* and *Vibrio*. Both conditions are best handled by prevention. All incoming crayfish must be inspected for signs of dermal ulceration, shell discoloration, or other signs of illness, and only apparently healthy animals should be permitted access to the breeding population. Depressed or obviously sick animals should be isolated from healthy ones and discarded. The elucidation of specific bacterial pathogens requires microbiological culture; these laboratory tests often greatly outweigh the value of the individual crayfish unless they are particularly valuable breeding stock or are being kept for experimental studies, in which case, treatment with appropriate antibiotic therapy might be justified on economic grounds. Once the particular bacteria or fungi are identified, specific antibiotic agents can be added to the tank water or in the food offered to the entire population, rather than treating individual animals.

Crayfish are highly prone to trauma induced by fighting with their tankmates. Much of this competition can be prevented by avoiding overcrowded conditions and segregating the animals by size. Furnishing the tanks with clay pipes or half-tiles as refuges into which the crayfish can retire will greatly lessen the incidence of fighting and cannibalism; these refuges also will permit a greater number of animals to be kept in a given tank space and volume.

6

Pulmonates

"Will you walk a little faster?"
said a whiting to a snail.
"There's a porpoise close behind us,
and he's treading on my tail."

Lewis Carroll
1832–1898

TERRESTRIAL SNAILS AND GIANT BANANA SLUGS

Although one would hardly think of a huge slug or snail as a conventional pet, these pulmonates (as snails and slugs are properly called) sometimes are kept as study animals. The simple nervous system of large "banana" slugs, *Ariolimax columbianus*, from the Pacific Northwest is being studied by comparative neurophysiologists. Their characteristic tenacious mucoid slime is being researched by adhesive materials biochemists because of its ability to adhere to many porous and nonporous materials and because of its biodegradability in the environment. Anyone who has handled banana slugs with bare hands knows just how difficult it can be to remove the slime once it has come into contact with skin. These creatures are relatively easy to keep in captivity and many live for several years. Although the common brown snail is relatively uniform in its coloration, banana slugs display a variety of colors and patterns (**Figures 49a & b**).

While I was engaged in an active exotic animal

Fig. 49a, page 106

Fig. 49b, page 106

75

Fig. 50a, page 106

Fig. 50b, page 106

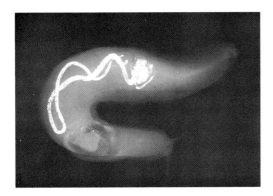

Figure 50c. In order to study the gastrointestinal tract of these animals, their fondness for strawberries was expolited. A suspension of barium contrast medium was mixed with fresh strawberry which the slug readily ingested. After a few minutes, an X-ray photographic image was obtained; the barium contrast medium has already passed through the stomach and into the intestine and caecum.

practice, "pet" garden snails, *Helix aspersa*, (and illegally obtained giant African snails, especially *Achatina fulica*) occasionally were presented by their concerned owners, most of whom were children. A side benefit of these encounters was that often the children had their first positive exposure to the veterinary profession. One notable example was a six or seven-year-old girl who many years later went on to become a veterinarian and credited my treatment of her pet snail as her impetus for choosing veterinary medicine as a career.

Today, the giant African terrestrial snail, *Achatina* can no longer be imported into the United States, but it has potential value as a protein resource in human diets in those areas where other sources of animal protein are deficient. From the aesthetic point of view, this large snail is no more loathesome than the edible crab, abalone, squid, octopus, oysters, and many other delicacies.

Housing

Glass jars and terraria are suitable homes for these animals. Snails and slugs can climb perpendicular or even inclined smooth glass surfaces. Forest litter, leaf mold or slightly moist sphagnum moss should be placed on the bottom of the container, and pieces of weathered tree bark or broken flower pot shards should be provided as hiding places. Sufficient hiding places will lessen the likelihood of the slugs crawling excessively over the inner glass surfaces; this will reduce the frequency of having to clean the slime trails from the glass.

These animals are most active during periods of low-light intensity and high relative humidity. A temperature of less than approximately 23 °C (73.4 °F) is preferred.

Nutrition

The alimentary system of these animals is relatively short and was displayed well in banana slug by the use of barium contrast radiography (Frye 1986) (**Figures 50a–c**).

The diet of the common brown garden snail, the exotic (and often illegal-to-possess) giant land snail, and most terrestrial slugs consists of moist edible leafy vegetables; fruits, especially banana peels and apples; small amounts of dry kibbled dog food; and poultry mash. The immense appetites and very short digestive tracts of these beasties enhance the amount of damage they can do to a garden in a short time and, therefore, an adequate food supply is imperative for captive snails and slugs. Fortunately, these molluscs can be fed wilted and overripe fruit that can be obtained *gratis* from many food markets.

Reproduction

Being truly hermaphoditic, each slug or snail possesses an erectile intromittant organ or penis that is inserted into the appropriate genital opening of its mate during copulation (**Figure 51a**). In this manner, each partner, having the same genital inventory, exchanges semen, with the other so that while they cannot fertilize themselves, each mates with the other and they both produce internally fertilized eggs. A clear mucoid spermatophore containing spermatozoa (**Figure 52**) is secreted during intromission; the spermatozoa fertilize the eggs within the oviduct. This plug also aids in the discuraging successful copulation with other snails (**Figures 51b**).

The eggs are deposited in moist forest litter hidden beneath slabs of bark or under broad leaves (**Figure 53**).

Fig. 51a, page 106

Fig. 51b, page 107

Fig. 52, page 107

Fig. 53, page 107

Medical Disorders

There are few specific or well-defined diseases of the pulmonates. Infection with *Aeromonas hydrophila*, the common bacterial pathogen of many so-called "cold-blooded" animals, has been described. The effects of rasping predators resulting in discolored or abnormally white lesions on the shell and soft tissues have been reported. *Mycobacterium* sp. have been isolated from some slugs and snails.

Molluscs may become infested with tiny external parasitic mites, but they appear to tolerate these parasites well. Some isopods (pillbugs, "sow" bugs) have been observed feeding on the tissues of living snails. If these insects are found to be preying on snails, they should be removed from the terrarium. Molluscs are very susceptible to osmotic alterations—as anyone who has sprinkled table salt on snail pests knows.

7

Turbellarians

"I write from a worm's eye point of view."

Ernie Pyle
1900–1945

AQUATIC AND TERRESTRIAL
FLATWORMS

During high school biology courses, most students are exposed to turbellarians. The common aquatic flatworm planaria were used to demonstrate chemoreceptive ability and orientation as well as the ability to regenerate parts of the body. These animals have been included in this discussion because they are employed so often in biology curricula, and children enjoy taking them home for study and manipulation. The rise in consciousness of animal welfare issues has made the use of vertebrates as biological subjects for study in elementary and high school curricula untenable.

The most commonly studied species of turbellarians are the aquatic *Euplanaria* (**Figure 54**), and *Leptoplana* and the much larger and terrestrial *Bipalium kewense* (**Figure 55**). The aquatic forms inhabit cool, clear, permanent bodies of fresh water such as streams, ponds, marshes, and springs, where they may be found clinging to the undersides of rocks, plants, and logs. They tend to hide during the daylight hours, but can be attracted to fresh meat baits anchored in their vicinity. The worm-like terrestrial turbellarians are often found after a heavy rain.

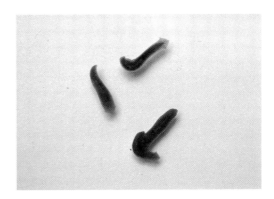

Figure 54. Three *Planaria* flatworms. These aquatic creatures are used often in teaching biology.

Fig. 55, page 107

In the laboratory, they can be induced to respond to weak galvanic, mechanical, and chemical stimuli and, thus, are useful as models in simple metazoan animal behavior.

Within the formless internal tissue of the body are uncommitted "formative cells" that, when stimulated, undergo multiplication and produce new parts in regeneration. It is the presence of these cells which can differentiate into more than one tissue or organ that these primitive organisms are of interest to biologists.

Housing

Aquatic turbellarians should be kept in clean fresh water contained in shallow vessels such as saucers, glass or plastic jars, or baking dishes. The pH of the water should be maintained at approximately 6.4 to 7.0 and must be free of dissolved chlorine. The pH may be tested with inexpensive test strips available from drug suppliers and aquarium stores. These strips will yield color changes at various pH levels; these correspond to various hydrogen ion concentrations. Whenever possible, use distilled water; municipal water can be used if it is allowed to stand overnight in an open container that will allow the dissipation of dissolved chlorine. The ph-adjusting chemicals available from aquarium stores and pet dealers are generally safe for planarians, but they must be mixed with water to the desired concentration before being added to the tank water. This will avoid chemical burns to the tank's inhabitants.

The terrestrial turbellarians should be housed in much the same fashion as snails and slugs. Multiple animals may be kept together.

Nutrition

Both aquatic and terrestrial forms will readily eat small pieces of fresh meat, chopped earthworms, soaked commercial kibbled dog, and some soft vegetable material such as soaked pelleted alfalfa. Only small portions should be fed at one time to avoid spoilage and water fouling.

Reproduction

Turbellarians are hermaphroditic. Although both testes and ovaries develop from formative cells in the same individual, most, if not all, of these animals are unable to fertilize themselves. However, they may reproduce *asexually* via a process termed "transverse fission" in which a worm constricts in two, usually behind its pharynx, and the missing parts on each portion regenerate via the differentiation of uncommitted pluripotential cells that possess the ability to form more than one kind of tissue.

When they reproduce sexually, two planarians bring their posterior ventral surfaces together and copulation is mutual; the penis of each is inserted into the genital orifice of the other. Following internal fertilization of the ova, several zygotes and many yolk cells are combined into a single capsule or egg shell that is deposited in the aquatic environment. The young do not go through larval stages, but resemble their parents on a much smaller scale.

Medical Disorders

Chlorine poisoning (and other chemical intoxication) are the only medical diseases of which I am aware. Of course, the water and soil environments MUST be kept clean to prevent the overgrowth of pathogenic bacteria and fungi that may be lethal to these flatworms.

Anesthesia

If they are to be used to demonstrate regeneration of body parts in a classroom setting, aquatic planarians can be anesthetized by exposing them to a 1:10,000 dilution of benzocaine. Once they have become narcotized, potentially painful procedures can be performed. Using anesthetized animals, even lowly worms, is recommended because of humane considerations. As soon as possible, they should be placed in fresh water. Arousal will occur within 10–15 minutes at room temperature. As a substitute, dilute ethanol can be used, but it is not as safe as benzocaine.

8

Culture of Prey Species

Several varieties of invertebrates are kept in captivity primarily as a food source for higher animals. This chapter will serve as a practical guide for the culture of such prey species.

Although earthworms, crickets, mealworms, and waxworms can be purchased from fish bait, pet, and aquarium dealers, and fruit flies and mulberry silk moth eggs and larvae ("silkworms") are available from biological supply firms, often it is more convenient and economical to raise these invertebrates at home or within the confines of a professional collection. They are not difficult to raise and often any surplus may be traded to fellow hobbyists, pet dealers, or aquarium stores for other items of interest.

EARTHWORMS

Good to eat, and wholesome to digest,
as a worm to a toad, a snake to a pig,
a pig to a man, and a man to a worm.

Ambrose Bierce
1842–1914

The common earthworm and its larger cousin, the "nightcrawler" (*Lumbricus terrestris*), are easily cultured. They require little care and their castings are a most useful additive to house and garden plants.

Housing

Earthworms are most conveniently raised in well-drained wooden, concrete block, plastic or *nongalvanized* metal trays or boxes filled with humus-enriched soil, leaf mold, well-composted manure, or planting mix that is kept slightly moist, but not soaking wet. Gaddie and Douglas in their books on earthworms mentioned the importance of not using resinous waste or compost. They specifically noted that the leaves, needles or bark of citrus, bay (laurel), conifers (pine, fir), redwood, sequoia, cedar, and eucalyptus should not be used because they may contain harmful aromatic oils or resins that can intoxicate earthworms or drive them away from their growing beds. Horse, cattle, rabbit, turkey, or other animal manures can be mixed with peat moss, discarded cardboard packing, thoroughly composted wood and paper pulp, and other organic wastes. If manures are used, they too must be thoroughly composted. However, animal feces should not be over two years old because the valuable plant fibers in overly composted manure may be too decomposed and may lead to soil and growth media compaction. Fresh manure should be leached with water to remove excess amounts of ammonia and other nitrogenous products.

The surface of the growing medium should be covered with moistened clean burlap sack cloth or corrugated cardboard slabs. The worms will tend to congregate beneath this cover, and are easily harvested as needed. A shading device should be placed over the growing bed to prevent overheating of the medium during hot summer months. The medium should be slightly moist, but not sodden. Drainage of the growing beds must be adequate to prevent flooding.

Nutrition

Earthworms eat the soil-humus mix, absorbing what they can and passing the balance through their digestive systems as castings. All that is required is to add some cornmeal, clean, salt-free table scraps, poultry mash, or horse manure to the growing medium occasionally. Contrary to popular belief, used coffee grounds or tea leaves are not beneficial to either earthworms or plants. If it is suitable, a vegetable or flower garden may be combined with earthworm culture—and excellent symbiosis.

Reproduction

Earthworms are hemaphroditic and mate through out most of the year, reaching a peak of activity during warm, moist weather, particularly at night. Two worms stretch out from their burrows and bring their ventral surfaces together, with the front ends pointing in opposite directions. A specialized structure, the *clitellum*, on each worm grips five segments of the other worm. Specialized stiff hair-like structrures called setae on each worm penetrate the body of the other to aid in holding the worms together. Each worm secretes a slime tube about itself, covering about twenty-seven of the worm's segments or somites. On each worm, a pair of seminal grooves forms along which masses of sperm pass to enter the seminal recepticles of the other. The worms now separate from each other. Each worm later produces capsules or cocoons containing fertilized and embryonating eggs. These cocoons slip from the bodies of each mated worm and, in doing so, assume the shape of lemons as the central tube portion closes. The egg capsules are deposited in damp soil, and the young worms soon emerge and grow into adults.

Medical Conditions

Earthworms may be infected with *Bacillus thuringienis*, several yeasts and fungi. There are no specific treatments; a few investigors have tried offering medicated feeds with mixed results. If local wild birds are taking too many worms from the growing beds, wire netting should be used to cover the trays or troughs. Lightweight removable frames can be built to individual requirements, using wood and ordinary hardware. These frames should be covered with screening or coarse hardware cloth to prevent birds from prematurely harvesting your crop of worms.

TRUE CRICKETS, MORMON "CRICKETS," AND SIMILAR INSECTS

Such stillness . . .
The cries of the cicadas
Sink into the rocks.

Matsuo Basho
1644–1694

The common house crickets, *Gryllus domesticus,* *Acheta domestica,* and the Mormon cricket, *Anabrus simplex* (actually a wingless form of grasshopper) are cultured as food prey for insectivorous animals such as large spiders, scorpions, some fish, lizards, some birds, moles, shrews, bats, etc. Similarly, *Stenopelmatus,* the Jerusalem cricket also known as "sand crickets," "*Niños de la Tierra,*" or "baby faces" and other forms of wingless grasshopper, can be cultured as prey for insectivorous predators. These insects should be manipulated with forceps or scoop-like devices because they can deliver a nasty bite on the fingers of an unwary handler.

Housing

These insects should be housed in wooden, plastic, or metal boxes or bins with tight-fitting, screened lids. Smaller numbers can be cultured in gallon jars, also fitted with screened screwcap tops. Clean soil, potting soil, or forest humus can be used as a bedding or litter medium into which these creatures can burrow. *Acheta* and *Gryllus* are usually kept in cages furnished with clean sand litter.

Corrugated cardboard carton material or papier maché egg packing material should be furnished in the enclosure to serve as both a hiding place and a nesting site (**Figure 56**). Because most of the wingless grasshoppers are secretive and nocturnal creatures, they prefer to construct shallow burrows beneath pieces of nonresinous treebark or weathered wood set into clean loamy soil or forest humus.

Fig. 56, page 107

Nutrition

Crickets are opportunistic feeders and are essentially omnivorous. They eat a variety of vegetables, high protein cereal, cornmeal, poultry mash, small portions of dry kibbled dog food—and *each other* if kept in overcrowded conditions or if they are not supplied with enough food or moisture. They obtain most of their moisture from what they eat, but also will drink water from shallow containers such as jar lids or bottle caps. One convenient means for furnishing water for them is to use a piece of clean cellulose sponge placed into a shallow vessel of water. The sponge will absorb water so the insects can drink easily without danger of toppling into the container and drowning. Because crickets will cannibalize their kin when other sources of food are unavailable, it is essential that edible food is always present in the culture containers in which these insects are raised. Also, under the stress of hunger, they have been known to attack sluggish or weakened predators such as small lizards. Placing a small amount of their preferred food in their predator's cage will help eliminate this hazard.

Reproduction

Fertilization is internal, and individual eggs are laid singly in the substrate or on the cardboard. All of these insects go through an incomplete metamorphosis before reaching maturity. Several nymphal stages follow periodic molts of the outgrown chitinous exoskeleton.

The baby crickets may be fed, as needed, to their predators or allowed to increase in size and numbers to augment the breeding population.

Medical Disorders

Like most insects, crickets are susceptible to the bacteria, *Aeromonus* sp., *Bacillus thuringienensis*, and *Vibrio* sp., *Baculovirus* and perhaps several other viruses, and the protozoan, *Nosema* sp. Maintaining a "closed" colony and sound hygienic practices are essential. A closed colony is one into which no other breeding animals may be admitted during the life of a particular cultivar. The reduction of stress caused by overcrowding, poor nutrition, temperature extremes, and territorial disputes greatly diminishes the likelihood of widespread and devastating infections that can decimate a colony.

MEALWORMS (MEAL BEETLE LARVAE)

I do not want to be a fly!
I want to be a worm!''
Charlotte Perkins Stetson Gilman
1860–1935

The common mealworm, *Tenebrio molitor*, has been raised for many years as fish bait and for feeding fish, amphibians, reptiles, birds, and small insectivorous mammals. It is usually the larvae that are employed as food items. These insects are an excellent example of a creature that requires a complete metamorphosis during its development. Some larvae that are obtained from commercial sources have been treated with juvenile hormone which induces larger than normal size; these larvae, may not finish their metamorphic development because of this hormone treatment. Untreated larvae, if allowed to develop, will eventually stop eating and, after a final larval molt, become pupae. After a period of from one to two weeks, the pupal case splits along its upper or dorsal surface and an adult beetle emerges ready to find a mate and begin the life cycle again.

Housing

Mealworms can be grown in metal, plastic, or glass containers that are flat and broad and fitted with screened covers that will prevent the escape of beetles and larvae and prevent the contamination of the growing medium by moths or other extraneous competitive insects. The surface of the growth medium should be covered with clean burlap sackcloth; this will serve as a hiding place and as a brooding area.

Nutrition

To produce mealworms that are nutritionally sound with respect, in particular, to calcium, the growing medium of wheat bran midlings should be supplemented with 15 percent alfalfa flakes, 20 percent high protein baby cereal, and approximately 15 percent dry poultry mash. Moisture is provided by adding a few halved fresh apples or potatoes to the medium. These pieces of vegetable or fruit should be exchanged for freshly cut material as they dry or grow moldy. Excess larvae can be stored in a refrigerator for several weeks if they are placed into plastic containers filled with clean bran.

Reproduction

Shortly after mating, the impregnated females deposit their fertile eggs in the substrate in which they are kept or upon dry burlap sack material. As the young larvae hatch out, they burrow down into the rich growing medium, and should be harvested by screening or picking as they are required to meet the demands of the collection.

Medical Disorders

Mealworms and the adult *Tenebrio* beetles are susceptible to several bacterial, mycotic, and viral pathogens: *Serratia marcescens, Monilia anisopliae, Baculovirus* and assorted beta endotoxins have been isolated from clinically abnormal mealworm larvae and adult beetles. The protozoan *Nosema* also may be a threat to a thriving culture. The larvae of several feral moth species and some beetles may attack a culture of meal beetle larvae and can decimate them. This predation can be prevented easily by covering the culture containers with tight-fitting fine screened lids through which even small moths and beetles cannot penetrate to deposit their tiny eggs. The lids, of course, will prevent escape of the meal beetles also.

SILKWORMS (MULBERRY SILK MOTH LARVAE)

First cultured approximately 3,000 years ago in Asia for their valuable silk, the mulberry silk moth, *Bombyx mori*, and its larvae (**Figure 57**) can be an

Fig. 57, page 107

extremely useful invertebrate to illustrate complete metamorphosis to students. These large, soft-bodied larvae may be used for feeding many large mygalomorph spiders, scorpions, and many carnivorous lizards and bird species. Captive insectivorus marmosets, bats, moles, shrews, doormice, and hedgehogs also find these plump larvae to their liking. These larvae are substantially more nutritious than an identical volume of crickets or meal beetle larvae (Frye and Calvert 1989a, 1989b). If deemed necessary, these moth larvae can be dusted with calcium carbonate or some similar calcium-rich product. Frye and Calvert (1989b; 1990) demonstrated that the calcium content of these sizable, soft-bodied insect larvae can be more than doubled by either feeding them calcium supplements or by applying a calcium suspension to their exterior surfaces just before feeding them to a predatory vertebrate.

Like other lepidopteran insects, these moths must conclude a complete metamorphosis before becoming sexually mature adults. After centuries of domestication and selective breeding for silk production and disease resistance, mulberry silk moths, despite the presence of otherwise normal appearing wings, are generally incapable of flight. They beat their wings actively, but only very rarely can they fly. This feature is particularly valuable in cultured insects.

Housing

The silk "worm" larvae of the mulberry silk moth should be kept in tightly screened wooden or plastic cages whose volume depends upon the number of larvae to be maintained at any one time. For a population of two dozen larvae, a 1 to 1 1/2 cubic foot enclosure is sufficient. When provided with an adequate supply of freshly picked or frozen mulberry leaves, these soft-bodied larvae grow rapidly and can be harvested as required for food prey. Dried mulberry leaves serve well as cage litter, but should be changed when they become soiled to prevent the accumulation of wastes. The tightly fitting screened lid is not to prevent escape of the silk moth larvae but, instead, to prevent the entrance of parasitic insects that might prey upon these valuable creatures.

Nutrition

Silkworms are highly adapted to thrive on a restricted diet of mulberry leaves. Whether these leaves are harvested from fruited or fruitless mulberry trees does not appear to make any significant difference to the larvae as long as the leaves are free from pesticide residues. Some heavier twigs or branches of the mulberry tree should be included so that the larvae have a place to distribute themselves, rest, or spin their silk-wound cocoons (**Figure 58a–d**).

Several artificial diets for feeding silk moth larvae have been developed which permit the year 'round culture of these valuable insects. The products which have been used for several years by the Department of Entomology at the University of California, Davis campus are available from the following sources:

Nihon Nosan Kogyo
Research Center
20–4 Hinoda 2–Chome
Funabashi, Chiba 273
Japan

Katakura Kogyo Co, Ltd.
Katakura-Kogyo
4–5–25 Chuo
Matsumoto 390
Japan

Kyodo Shiryo Co., Ltd.
11–6–2 Gontazaka
Hodogaya-ku
Yokohama 240
Japan

Bio-Serv Co.
P.O. Box 450
Frenchtown, N.J.
08825
1-800-473-2155

Water

When fed fresh mulberry leaves, silkworms obtain their required moisture from their diet. When frozen leaves are fed, additional water can be provided by lightly misting the leaves once or twice daily. The leaves must not be allowed to become soggy because this will promote the growth of harmful fungi.

Reproduction

Fascinatingly, the silk moth was one of the first creatures in which artificial insemination was studied; the great eighteenth century physician and comparative zoologist, John Hunter, published the results of his experiments nearly 200 years ago (Hunter 1792);

Figure 58c. After their few weeks of active feeding and several molts, the larvae commence their labors by constructing a hammock-like sling and then spin their oval cocoons from a single strand of fine silk that measures approximately 1.6 kilometers (1 mile) in length. This prodigious spinning requires at least 24 hours. A dozen cocoons are illustrated.

Fig. 58a, page 108

Fig. 58b, page 108

Fig. 58d, page 108

Fig. 58e, page 108

Fig. 58f, page 108

Fig. 58g, page 108

also see Clarke (1990) for more details of this seminal work.

The mulberry silk moths mate soon after they emerge from their cocoons (**Figure 58e–f**). It is for this reason that a few larvae should be allowed to complete their metamorphosis. Although the males die shortly after they mate, the females may survive for several days and usually will deposit multiple clutches of eggs. Soon after mating, the female moths deposit their eggs onto mulberry twigs, leaves, discarded cocoons, or any other convenient surface. Fertile eggs are grey; infertile eggs remain pale yellow (**Figure 58g**).

If a supply of fresh mulberry leaves is available—or if an unlimited supply of frozen leaves can be stored properly—a nearly year 'round culture of larvae can be provided.

Medical Disorders

There are several pathogenic viruses, particularly *Reovirus* and *Fijivirus*, that have been isolated from infected silk moth larvae. One severe, often endemic, disease of these insects is *cytoplasmic polyhedrosis virus* infection. This RNA virus is transmitted from infected larvae to susceptible silkworms via the ingestion of infected material deposited on mulberry leaves. This virus attacks the lining of the intestine; very soon after infection, the larvae begin to lose condition from diminished absorption of nutrients from the intestine. There is no specific medical treatment for this condition.

Several gram-negative bacteria and the protozoan *Nosema bombycis* have also been isolated from these insects. If morbidity or multiple death losses are noted, the population should be discarded and the culture container thoroughly cleansed before new larvae or adults are introduced. Steam autoclaving is highly effective for disinfection.

Some wasps employ the larvae of the silk moth as hosts upon which to lay their eggs. The female wasps sting their prey, and although their venom does not kill the insect, it causes paralysis. After they hatch, the developing wasp larvae feed upon the immobilized silk moth caterpillars, eventually killing them. Screening the culture container prevents this depredation.

WAXWORMS (WAX MOTH LARVAE)

Instead of dirt and poison we have chosen to fill our hives
with honey and wax; thus furnishing mankind with the two
noblest of things, which are sweetness and light.

Jonathan Swift
1667–1745

The wax moth, *Galleria mellonella*, and the lesser bee moth, *Achroia grisella*, are predators of honey bees' brood combs. Frequently, these combs are deserted, but if wax moths attempt to enter an occupied beehive, a healthy colony of bees usually is able to combat and repel the depreciations of these insects. The larvae of these moths have been cultured as prey for insectivorous invertebrates and vertebrates.

Culture Medium for Newly Hatched Wax Moth Larvae

boiling water	100 ml
glycerine, U.S.P.	100 ml
honey	100 ml
vitamin supplement (Vionate or Avitron)	5 gm or 5ml respectively
infant cereal	1,200 gm
calcium proprionate*	1.5 gm

*Catalog number 1053347 Eastman Kodak Co., Inc.

Bake the cereal at 200 °F for 2 hours. Mix the liquid ingredients together. Add vitamin supplement and calcium proprionate, mixing well. Add liquids to cereal, mixing thoroughly to distribute all the ingredients. Store in glass jars.

This growth medium is used to feed moth larvae until they can be transferred to a less refined diet.

Diet for Larger Larvae

miller's bran	1,200 ml (dry measure)
honey	200 ml

water	100 ml
glycerine, U.S.P.	9 ml
brewer's yeast	1 tablet
vitamin supplement	(Vionate, or Avitron 5 gm or 5ml, respectively
calcium proprionate*	1.5 gm

*Catalog number 1053347 Eastman Kodak Co., Inc.

Bake the miller's bran at 200 °F for 2 hours. Thoroughly mix dry ingredients with liquid ingredients until homogeneous.

Place 2–4 tablespoons of the medium into one-gallon, wide-mouth glass pickle, mayonnaise, or mustard jars. Place half-grown 0.5 cm (1/4 inch) or larger larvae into each jar, and cover the top of the container with one or more layers of cotton gauze or nylon stocking material.

Depending upon the size of the culture and its container, and the number of larvae (or adult moths) that are required, 2–10 pairs are used to start a culture. Place culture jars in an environmental temperature of about 27.7 to 34 °C (82–94 °F). The larvae will mature and pupate within approximately two weeks, and the moths will soon emerge to mate and produce another generation.

The sexes are easy to determine because the male moths are significantly smaller than females.

A piece of accordion-pleated filter or wax paper placed will the jar will mimic a brood comb and afford the moths a place upon which to deposit their fertilized eggs. If the demand is sufficiently large, starting the culture jars should be staggered so that a continual supply of larvae and moths will be available.

FRUIT FLY AND HOUSEFLY CULTURE

Aesop's Fly, sitting on an axle of a chariot, has been much laughed at for exclaiming: "What a dust I do raise!"
Thomas Carlyle
1795–1881

To some readers, it might seem strange to actually go out of one's way to produce creatures that are common household pests. As anyone who has ever shopped in the produce section of a supermarket knows, fruit flies are frequently present—particularly if ripe pineapples or bananas are on display. An hour or two after you bring these fruits home, you may find these tiny insects swarming around your fruit bowl.

For students of biology or genetics, the fruit fly, *Drosophila melanogaster*, has been one of the primary animal models for the study of Mendelian inheritance. The successful culture of newly hatched or newly born tiny insectivorous lizards, praying mantids, spiders, etc. demands a steady supply of small soft-bodied insects. The discovery and selective propagation of genetically wingless forms of fruit flies now make it possible to produce any number of flightless insects that can only crawl about. The culture medium upon which these flies grow adds necessary nutrients to the insectivores' diets also by improving the chemical composition of the prey.

These flies are cultured on a modified formula that has been employed at the Department of Genetics at the University of California, Davis, and described by Morris (1983). Other growth media can be obtained from the biological supply firms listed later in this text.

Culture Medium Formula

agar	18 gm
brewer's yeast	28 ml
cornmeal	56 ml
dextrose	126 ml
sucrose	665 ml
warm water	500 ml
boiling water	1,000 ml
calcium proprionate*	9 ml

*Catalog number 1053347 Eastman Kodak Co., Inc.

Morris stated that the dextrose/sucrose mixture could be replaced by substituting 125 ml molasses or 125 ml of a 50:50 molasses/liquid dextrose or Karo syrup mix.

Mix the dry ingredients and store in a cool place until needed to make a fresh batch of growing medium. When required, add warm water to dissolve the sugar/syrup mix so that the resulting solution does not contain lumps. Then add the agar, brewer's yeast, and cornmeal. Meanwhile boil the water. Pour the diluted sugar/syrup/agar/yeast/cornmeal mix into the boiling water, stir well, and allow to cool. After it is sufficiently cool to handle comfortably, pour the mixture into 50 ml glass vials, taking particular care to avoid splashing the culture medium onto the sides of the vials. The recipe above is sufficient to produce approximately 200 vials. Place a piece of tissue paper or lens tissue into the medium to afford the fly larvae a place upon which to pupate. The open end of the vials should be closed with a cotton ball wrapped in a piece of cotton gauze or nylon stocking.

Various strains of fruit flies can be purchased from any of several biological supply firms. If only a few flies are needed, a call to the genetics department of most local colleges or universities might result in a starter culture. As mentioned before, the genetically wingless or vestigial winged (vg) strains are preferable to ones that can fly.

Breeding occurs in the vials, so to "inoculate" an uncultivated vial, pour a few adult flies from a thriving vial into each freshly prepared vial. The generation time of these insects is brief; to produce a steady supply of flies, plan to inoculate a new set of vials about every 5–7 days. The number of vials to be incubated will depend upon the demand for flies. Actively crawling flies can be slowed or immobilized by placing the vials in the refrigerator for a few minutes.

Larger houseflies, including *Musca domestica*, can be raised on artificial culture media much like that described above, but some form of high quality animal protein such as meat extract should be added, as described by Morris (1983). Of course, a much larger culture container must be employed. The old-fashioned glass milk or cream bottles with large-diameter tops are excellent for this purpose. The tops of these containers should be stoppered with gauze-covered cotton that will confine the flies, yet permit adequate air circulation.

Although the culture of fruit flies is not necessarily accompanied by an unpleasant odor, the production of housefly maggots can be associated with a foul smell because the meat extract-containing medium, maggots themselves and their wastes have a disagreeable odor.

A modified culture technique has been employed by the Department of Nematology at the University of California, Davis. It was described by Morris (1983) and is printed here with further modifications. The volume of the diet placed into culture vials and the size of the culture containers is necessarily predicated upon the number and size of the larvae. These media may be available from commercial sources; they are printed here for those readers who cannot obtain them from biological supply firms.

Appendix: Commercial Sources for Some Living Invertebrates

ARMSTRONG'S CRICKET FARM
P. O. Box 125
West Monroe, Lousiana 71294
1-318-387-6000

CAROLINA BIOLOGICAL SUPPLY COMPANY
Main Office and Laboratory
Burlington, North Carolina 27215
1-919-584-0381
1-800-334-5551

and

POWELL LABORATORIES DIVISION
Gladstone, Oregon 97027
1-656-1641
1-800-547-1733

CENTER FOR REPTILE AND AMPHIBIAN
PROPAGATION
5645 W. San Madele, Suite # 103
Fresno, CA 93722
1-209-276-1031

GRUBCO, INC.
P. O. Box 15001
Hamilton, OH 45015
1-800-222-3563

HOGTOWN HERPETOLOGICAL SUPPLY, INC.
1801 N. E. 23rd Avenue
Gainesville, FL 32609
1-904-338-0504

NILES BIOLOGICAL LIVE CULTURES AND
SPECIMENS
9298 Elder Creek Road
Sacramento, CA 95829
1-916-386-2665

QUALITY VENOMS FOR MEDICAL RESEARCH
6850 Cleveland Drive
Punta Gorda, FL 33982
1-813-575-1775

WARD'S NATURAL SCIENCE ESTABLISHMENT
5100 W. Henrietta Road
P. O. Box 92912
Rochester, NY 14692-9012
1-716-359-2902

WESTERN SCIENTIFIC SUPPLY CO.
Division of Esten Scientific Co., Inc.
1705 So. River Road
P. O. Box 681
West Sacramento, CA 95691
1-916-371-2705

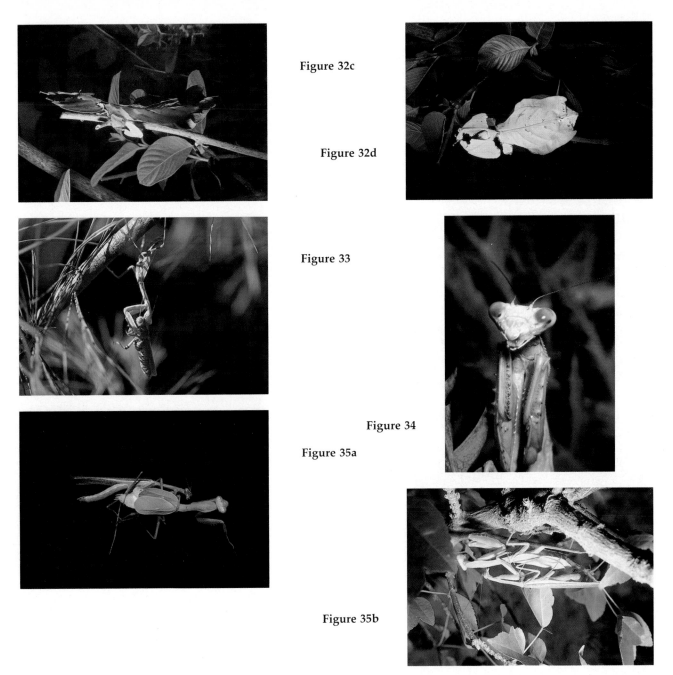

Figure 32c

Figure 32d

Figure 33

Figure 34

Figure 35a

Figure 35b

Figures 32c & d. Some tropical mantises are equipped with leaf-like extensions which camouflage them in their rain forest habitat. Both of these leaf mantises were photographed in Singapore. Note the leaf-like ribs and brown spots which so closely mimic foliage.

Figures 33. Able to subdue insects that equal or even exceed her body weight and size, this female mantis holds a large locust in her firm grip as he begins to devour it with her sharp mandibles and maxillae.

Figure 34. Always on the lookout for a male which may serve the dual purposes of mate and meal—the female mantis of this species has brilliant lavender eyes.

Figure 35a & b. If he is successful in finding a potential mate who is not hungry, the male mantis may be able to accomplish his amorous mission and escape with his life. In this photograph made in the author's laboratory, the males have restrained the female's body and wings, but can still be attacked if she suddenly turns and employs her highly modified first pair of legs.

Figure 36a

Figure 36b

Figure 37a

Figure 38

Figure 39a

Figure 39b

Figures 36a & b. Sometimes, however, the male mantis is captured and loses his head for his efforts. This apparent calamity does not interfere with the male's purpose in life's scheme. As his head and neck are severed, he also loses a specialized organ (the subesophageal ganglion) which, interestingly, acts to inhibit his mating activity. As this inhibition is removed, the now headless male is free to perform his necessary function to pass on his genes to his progeny.

Figure 37a. Within a few days, the fertilized female begins to construct one or more bread loaf shaped foam nests into which she deposits about three dozen elongated eggs. The foam soon hardens into a firm insulating material that will protect the undeveloped eggs during the winter. After forming these nests and depositing her eggs, the female mantis dies. The foam nest can be fastened on tree branches and house walls.

Figure 38. After surviving the winter's cold, the long-dormant eggs are finally warmed by spring weather and soon hatch into tiny wingless replicas of their parents. Here, hatchling mantis nymphs look for their first meal—often settling for their less wary siblings.

Figure 39a. Mating pair of phasmatid stick insects photographed in Forida. Photo by Dr. Salvatore Zeitlin.

Figure 39b. Other phasmatid stick and phylliitid leaf insects, have evolved protective structures and coloration to mimic the environment in which they live. Some look very much like leaves, with leaf-like veins and blighted spots, and are nearly impossible to discern from natural foliage or twigs. The leaf insects illustrated are in the family Phylliididae. The adult females measure over 16 cm in length (nearly 6 inches) and have vestigial, nonfunctional wings. The mature males of this species may exceed 11 cm (4 1/4 inches) but are much more slender and possess functional wings. Note the oval egg that this female is just about to deposit.

102

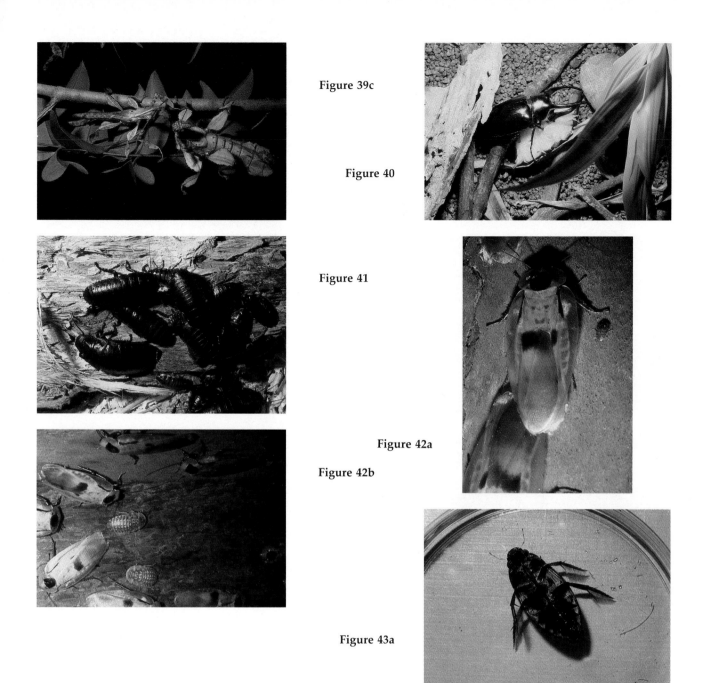

Figure 39c

Figure 40

Figure 41

Figure 42a

Figure 42b

Figure 43a

Figure 39c. Other phasmatid stick and phylliitid leaf insects, have evolved protective structures and coloration to mimic the environment in which they live. Some look very much like leaves, with leaf-like veins and blighted spots, and are nearly impossible to discern from natural foliage or twigs. The leaf insects illustrated are in the family Phylliididae. The adult females measure over 16 cm in length (nearly 6 inches) and have vestigial, nonfunctional wings. The mature males of this species may exceed 11 cm (4 1/4 inches) but are much more slender and possess functional wings.

Figure 40. Some of the world's largest insects are native to tropical rain forests. Illustrated is a Malaysian rhinoceros beetle whose enormous size can be seen in comparison to the half pineapple which it is eating.

Figure 41. Wingless hissing cockroaches from Madagascar. These impressive slow moving insects are frequently displayed in invertebrate collections. Note the several stages or instars illustrated in this photograph.

Figure 42a & b. Enormous winged cockroaches, such as these *Blaberus gigantea*, are popular attractions in invertebrate collections. These insects measured 8 cm (3 inches) in length. Some tropial cockroaches are even larger. Note the several nymphal stages alongide the adults.

Figure 43a. The underside of this large water beetle is covered with tiny hair-like extensions which trap a thin layer of air which furnishes oxygen to this actively swimming creature. The paler colored areas represent this "plastron" mechanism. As a further modification for their aquatic habits the limbs of this water beetle are elongated and equipped with fringes of short stiff hairs which increase the surface area and aid in the swimming ability of these insects.

103

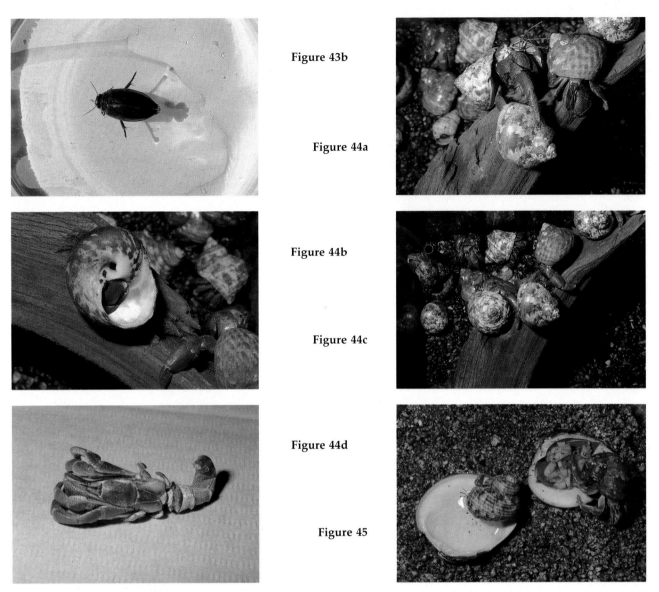

Figure 43b

Figure 44a

Figure 44b

Figure 44c

Figure 44d

Figure 45

Figure 43b. The rear-most limbs of this "waterboatman" beetle are elongated into oar-like sweeps with which these insects propel themselves rapidly through the water in pursuit of prey.

Figure 44a. Terrestrial hermit crabs, *Coenobita clypeatus* have become increasingly popular terrarium pets. Often, the seashells that these crabs inhabit are more valuable than the crabs themselves.

Figure 44b. The entrance to their borrowed snail shells can be blocked effectively by their greatly enlarged chelate pedipalp.

Figure 44c. These crustaceans are agile climbers and can escape if inclining rough surfaces permit access to the top of their terrarium.

Figure 44d. Hermit crabs are coiled to fit snugly into their adopted snail shell homes. Note the left hand twist that is illustrated in this dead hermit crab that has been removed from its shell.

Figure 45. Being omnivorous, these crabs are easy to feed. A small amount of slightly saline water provides much-needed moisture for these animals to bathe their gills.

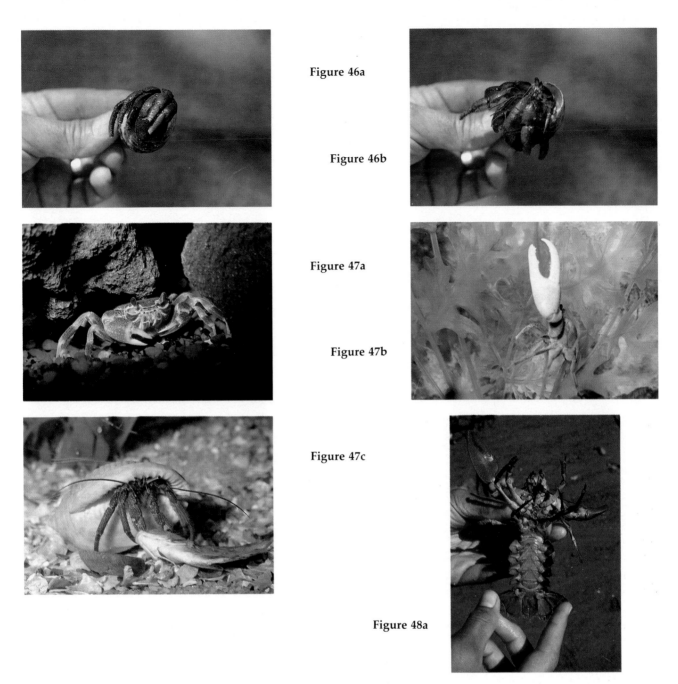

Figure 46a

Figure 46b

Figure 47a

Figure 47b

Figure 47c

Figure 48a

Figure 46a & b. Hermit crabs must be handled carefully to avoid the well-developed pincer-like pedipalp. Here in an instant, the crab has sought the fingertip of the author.
Figure 47a–c. Aquatic crabs often are brightly colored and earn their living in the aquarium by consuming waste food and detritus. Some look much like small version of edible crabs; others have one enormous fiddle-like pedipalp; yet others, like their terrestrial cousins, inhabit abandoned sea shells.
Figure 48a. A large crayfish handled properly to avoid being pinched by the large pincers.

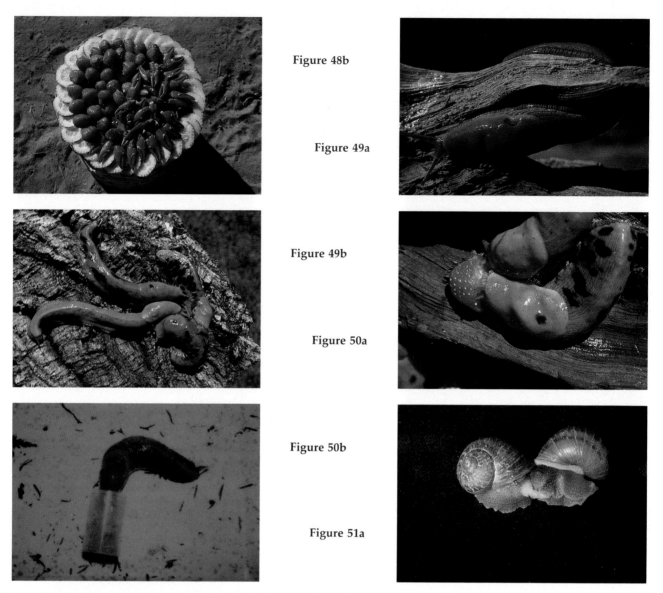

Figure 48b. Small numbers of these crustaceans can be kept together with other aquatic animals in fresh water aquaria.

Figures 49a & b. Even slugs can be kept as pets or study animals. These large "banana" slugs native, to the Pacific northwest to the latitude of southern British Columbia, are fascinating creatures that offer the comparative biologist much to study. They may be any of several colors and patterns. Their mucoid surface is in stark contrast to the dry bark upon which they are crawling.

Figure 50a & b. In order to study the gastrointestinal tract of these animals, their fondness for strawberries was expoited. A suspension of barium contrast medium was mixed with fresh strawberry which the slug readily ingested. After a few minutes, an X-ray photographic image was obtained; the barium contrast medium has already passed through the stomach and into the intestine and caecum.

Figure 51a. Pulmonates are hermaphroditic. Although each animal possesses both male and female sex organs, they seek out another of their kind when they mate; each exchanges gametes with its partner. In this series of photographs, two snails approach each other, insert an intromittant organ into the other, exchange semen in the form of a packet-like spermatophore, and separate.

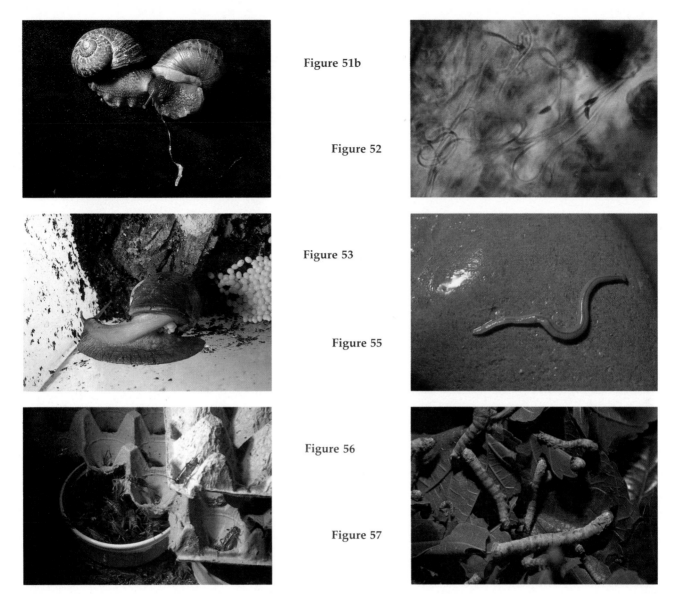

Figure 51b

Figure 52

Figure 53

Figure 55

Figure 56

Figure 57

Figure 51b. Pulmonates are hermaphroditic. Although each animal possesses both male and female sex organs, they seek out another of their kind when they mate; each exchanges gametes with its partner. In this series of photographs, two snails approach each other, insert an intromittant organ into the other, exchange semen in the form of a packet-like spermatophore, and separate.

Figure 52. Snail and slug spermatozoa are similar in size and shape to those of higher animals. This specimen was stained with new methylene blue stain and photographed at a 268 magnification.

Figure 53. A giant snail, *Achatina fulica* depositing its eggs. Photo by John E. Cooper, F.R.C.V.S..

Figure 55. A terrestrial turbellarian, *Bipalium kewense*. These flatworms are found most often beneath moist forest litter or on pavements during or after a sustained rain shower. Although they have been thought to be external parasites, they are harmless to humans and domestic animals.

Figure 56. Relatively large numbers of crickets can be cultured together as long as adequate vertical and horizontal surfaces are provided for the insects to distribute themselves. The use of cardboard egg carton material as resting and nesting sites is illustrated.

Figure 57. The mulberry silk moth, *Bombyx mori*, is one of the most economically important seasonal insects to be cultured for biological study and as prey for a variety of insectivorous predators. Actively feeding silk moth larvae. In this photograph larvae of both the light grey Asian and the black-ringed Spanish larvae are illustrated.

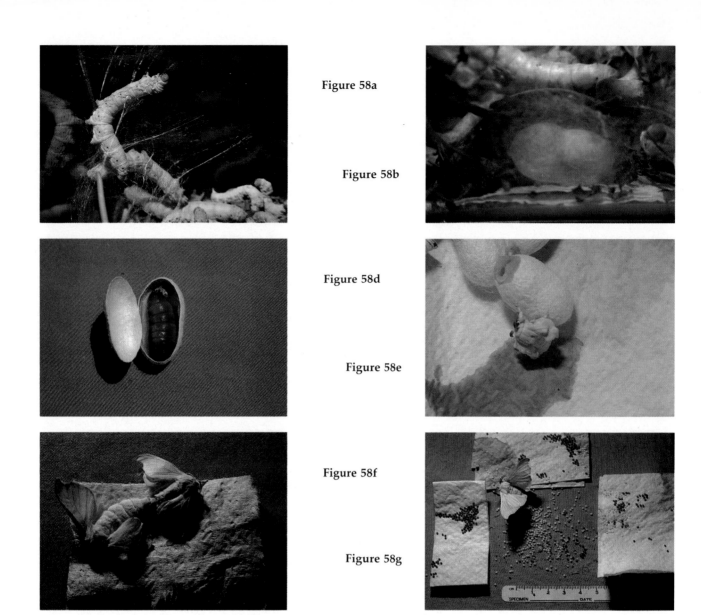

Figure 58a

Figure 58b

Figure 58d

Figure 58e

Figure 58f

Figure 58g

Figures 58a & b. After their few weeks of active feeding and several molts, the larvae commence their labors by constructing a hammock-like sling and then spin their oval cocoons from a single strand of fine silk that measures approximately 1.6 kilometers (1 mile) in length. This prodigious spinning requires at least 24 hours. A dozen cocoons are illustrated in Figure 58c.

Figure 58d. A cocoon is opened to reveal the pupa within. Note the wrinkled remnant of the last larval cuticle which was molted when the larvae had completed its cocoon.

Figures 58e–g. Just before emerging from confinement, these moths leave their pupal cases by secreting a drop or two of a silk-dissolving fluid and push through the now softened cocoons. Note the moist opening at the end of the the cocoon through which this moth has just emerged. Immediately after leaving the cocoon, they eject a stream of brown fluid waste, expand and dry their much-folded wings, and seek mates. Within a few hours after mating, the female silk moths begin to deposit some of the several hundred eggs that they produce during the next day or two. The males die a day or two after mating; the females die after three or four days. Fertile eggs are grey, infertile ones remain a pale yellow.

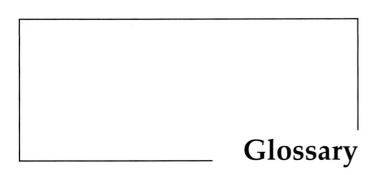

Glossary

alopecia: hair loss, baldness.

amphigonia retardata: delayed fertilization resulting from the union of previously inseminated and stored spermatozoa with freshly ovulated eggs.

anorexia: loss of appetite.

anterior: the front of an animal.

aquatic: water-dwelling.

arboreal: tree-dwelling.

arolium: the sucker or adhesive organ present on the end of the pedipalps of solifugid arachnids.

arthropod: jointed leg or foot; a class of invertebrates possessing jointed limbs.

cannibal, cannibalism: feeding upon one's own species.

carapace: the hard, often curved plate that covers all or part of the upper surface of some arachnids.

carnivorous: meat-eating; organisms that feed upon animal tissues.

carrion: dead, often rotting cadaverous body tissue.

caudal: referring to the tail-end of an animal.

cephalothorax: the combined head and midbody portion of many arachnids such as spiders.

chelicerae: claw-like chewing mouthparts of many arthropods.

chitin: an insoluble organic substance from which the exoskeletons of many invertebrates is formed. This material consists of one or more polysaccharides formed from numbers of glucosamine units that are closely linked. It is not digestible by most vertebrates.

chrysalis: the cocoon in which many insects undergo their final developmental stages during complete metamorphosis from worm-like grubs to sexually mature adults.

clitellum: a conspicuous glandular swelling from which cocoons containing fertilized eggs are formed and shed by earthworms.

coelom: the cavity that normally surrounds the intestine and other body organs.

commensal: a form of nonparasitic symbiotic relationship where one organism feeds with another; neither organism harms the other.

complete metamorphosis: a biological process during which an organism undergoes substantial morphological change from an immature larval form to the adult form.

compost: aerobically decomposed waste organic matter. This material may be of plant or animal origin, but usually refers to vegetation.

courtship: the period or activity before copulation during which the male and female participate in ritualized movements and/or postures in order to lower the resistance to mating.

coxa: the most proximal or innermost portion of an arthropod's limb or appendage.

crepuscular: preferring twilight; active in subdued light.

crustacean: arthropod animal of the class Crustacea such as crayfish, crabs, lobsters, etc.

cuticle: the outer covering of invertebrates forming the superficial exoskeleton.

cytology: the study of cells.

dermal: referring to the skin layer beneath the epidermis.

dimorphic: having two distinct forms; usually refers to the differences observed between the two sexes.

diurnal: preferring daylight; active during the day.

diverticulum: a blindly ending or pouch-like region of the gut or other hollow tubular organ.

dorsal: pertaining to the back of an animal; the uppermost surface that is directed away from the substrate upon which the animal is resting.

dysecdysis: difficult or faulty shedding or molting of the outer covering tissues.

ecdysis: the normal shedding, molting or sloughing of the exoskeleton.

ecology: the study of the interrelationship between organisms and their environments.

ectoparasite: an organism living on the outside of the body of its host.

endoparasite: an organism living inside the body of its host.

epizootic: an infectious disease among animals that may spread rapidly; it may affect a large number of individuals within a single or several different species, including humans.

esophagus: the portion of the alimentary canal between the pharynx and the midgut.

esturine: referring to an estuary or an aquatic area where the tide meets a river.

evolution: the process by which organisms have changed from ancestral to modern forms.

excretion: the process by which waste products of metabolism are removed from an organism.

exoskeleton: an external, rather than internal, (and usually nonbony) skeleton; often contains chitin. Seen in insects and many other invertebrates.

external digestion: the digestive processing of food material outside the alimentary canal before it is swallowed. This process is also termed "extraoral digestion."

external fertilization: the union of sperm and egg that takes place outside of the mother's body.

exudate: usually refers to a substance excreted from tissue as a result of disease.

foliage: leaves, flowers and twigs or branches of plants.

fossorial: living a subterranean life; preferring to dig or burrow beneath the surface.

free-living: referring to an animal that does not live on or within another animal; not a parasite, symbiont, or commensal relationship.

gamete: a mature reproductive cell; in the male, the gametes are called sperm or spermatozoa; in the female, the gametes are called eggs or ova.

gastropod: literally stomach-footed; a mollusc such as a snail, slug or single-valve shelled animal.

gonad: the gamete-producing glandular organ of a plant or animal.

gonopore: reproductive opening.

guanine: the nitrogenous waste product of arachnids; synonymous with urine or urates in higher animals.

haemocoel: the body cavity of invertebrates through which a fluid, the haemolymph, flows.

haemolymph: a clear tissue fluid in invertebrates that serves the function of blood.

hexapod: possessing six legs.

homologous: a term describing one or more structures in different organisms that may possess the same or different functions but have a similar origin.

humus: decomposed and composted organic matter.

hyperthermia: a condition of being overheated.

hypothermia: a condition of being chilled, underheated.

imago: the adult stage of an insect.

immobilize: to render incapable of voluntary movement.

incomplete metamorphosis: a biological process during which an organism undergoes minor change from an immature nymphal or immature form to the adult; a worm- caterpillar; or grub-like stage usually is lacking.

ingestion: the taking of food into the body.

insemination: the transfer of spermatozoa from the male to the female.

instar: a stage of development of arthropod invertebrates between two successive ecdyses or molts.

internal fertilization: the union of sperm and egg inside the body of the mother. Sperm are inseminated into the female's genital system by the male's penis, or by the uptake of a spermatophore that has been deposited by a male.

invertebrate: lacking a vertebral column or spine.

isopod: an insect whose legs are of equal length.

labrum: the upper lip of arthropods.

larva: immature form of an animal, usually undeveloped sexually.

lateral: referring to the side or flank of an animal.

lepidopteran: referring to possessing scaly wings; moths and butterflies are lepidopteran insects.

lumen: the cavity within a hollow organ, especially the gut.

maggot: a worm- or grub-like larva of an insect, especially flies.

Malpighian tubule: the excretory tubule of many in-vertebrate arthropods that arises from the midgut/hindgut boundary and extends into the haemocoel.

marine: living in the sea.

mastication: chewing; mechanical breaking down of food by means of the mouthparts or associated structures.

metabolism: the biochemical reactions taking place within the animal by which complex chemicals are converted into simple ones; the resulting release of energy is used for the activities of the organism and the synthesis of its tissues.

metamerically segmented: the serial repetition of body parts along the longitudinal axis.

metamorphosis: a major developmental process during which an organism changes from a larval form to the adult form.

mimicry: the superficial resemblance to other animals or to natural objects within the environment. This may serve as camouflage or a close resemblance to another creature.

mollusc: a noncrustacean shellfish; snails, slugs, clams, oysters, mussels, octopus, squid, and cuttlefish are members of the phylum Mollusca.

molt: the periodic shedding or sloughing of the exoskeleton.

morphological: referring to form and structure.

multicellular: an organism possessing more than one cell. May refer to either the plant or animal kingdom.

mygalognath: literally large + jaw; a group of particularly large, usually hairy spider-like arachnids, such as the tarantula; these are also called mygalomorphs.

nocturnal: preferring night time activity.

nonselective pesticide: a toxic substance which will eradicate good as well as noxious plants or animals.

nymph: a larval, sexually immature form or stage of an animal.

ocelli: eye-like photoreceptors found in many invertebrates, especially arthropods.

opisthosoma: the middle, "abdomen" division of most arachnids.

opportunistic: seizing the occasion to act, as in feeding upon whatever is available.

organoleptic: referring to the reception and perception of scents or flavors.

orthognath: from straight + jaw; referring to possessing straight, rather than angled or curved jaws.

ovary: the gonad of a female organism; the gland from which the female germ cells, eggs or ova, are produced and released.

oviduct: the tubular organ from which ova are transported from the ovary to the female genital opening; in many animals, the oviduct is the site where fertilization occurs.

oviparous: egg-laying.

oviposition: the process of egg laying.

ovoviviparous: the retention of the fertilized ova within the genital tract of the female parent until the time it exits as a partially or completely developed offspring; the nutrients are stored as yolk and are not transferred to the young from the maternal parent via placental membranes.

parasite: an animal that lives on or within the body of another organism, called the host and feeds upon it at the expense of the host.

parthogenesis: the asexual production of young by a unisexual population or one in which males are extremely rare. An example is the aphid insects.

pedipalp: literally foot + feeler; usually a jointed short leg-like portion of the mouthparts of many invertebrates, especialy spiders.

pectines: comb-like sense organ appendages on the underside of scorpions. They are thought to be sensitive to vibration and scent.

pH: a symbol used in expressing the hydrogen ion concentration of a substance; the degree of acidity or alkalinity of a solution.

pheromone: a chemical scent or cue secreted by one organism to which another organism of the same species responds either physiologically or psychologically. Many pheromones mediate or facilitate a sexual response in members of the opposite sex.

phoresy: one animal is used for transportation of another. This behavior is most often observed in small pseudoscorpions, mites, and insects.

physiology: the study of the processes which take place within an organism.

pygidium: a tail-like appendage found in some arachnids.

posterior: referring to the hind region of an organism; synonymous with caudal.

predator: an organism that preys upon another; usually refers to animals.

prey: an animal which is eaten by a predator.

prosoma: the anterior or "head" division of most arachnids; may form a "cephalothorax" in which each somite carries an appendage, such as the paired chelicerae, pedipalps, or walking legs.

proximal: referring to the point of origin of a part or organ.

pupa: the chrysalis or cocoon-like case in which the larvae of some insect complete their metamorphosis from an immature grub-, caterpillar; or worm-like creature to the adult form.

respiration: the exchange of oxygen and carbon dioxide between an organism and its environment.

riparian: referring to a streamside habitat.

riverine: referring to the habitat which exists in or alongside a river.

scavenger: an animal which feeds on the remains of animals or plants.

scutigera: an order of centipedes characterized by their seventeen pairs of very long spider-like legs, long antennae, and insect-like compound eyes.

sedentary: referring to an inactive, relatively immobile existence.

sense organs: specialized organs for the perception of stimuli from the external environment.

slough: the molting or shedding of all or part of the epidermal covering or exoskeleton; usually occurs periodically.

somite: one of the transverse segments into which the body of many invertebrates is divided.

sonotactic: sensitive to and responding to vibrations.

sonotropic: moving toward or away from the source of sound vibrations.

species: a natural population which interbreed freely to produce viable offspring and which resemble each other constantly in morphological and physiological features.

spermatophore: literally seed + to carry; a packet of

male gametes (spermatozoa) that is transferred to the female of the species as part of the early reproductive process.

spermatozoa: male sex cells or gametes.

spinerets: the slightly elongated organs through which silken threads are extruded by some invertebrates, especially but not limited to spiders.

spiracle: the external opening of the tracheal respiratory system in arthropods.

subesophageal: beneath the esophagus or gullet; refers to one or more organs located just below the esophagus of some insects such as the praying mantis.

substrate: the surface upon which an organism grows or is kept; litter material.

suctorial: possessing a sucking action.

symbiont: an organism living with another; not necessarily parasitic in nature.

tactile: referring to the sense of touch.

taxonomy: the study of classification of organisms.

telson: the bulbous organ bearing a sharp and recurved sting at the end of the metasoma or "tail" of a scorpion.

temperate: moderate; in the context of this usage, it refers to temperature.

testis: the male gonad that produces gametes called spermatozoa.

terrestrial: referring to the earth; living on the soil; neither aquatic nor arboreal (tree-dwelling).

thermoreceptor: a sense organ concerned with detecting temperature changes.

trachea: respiratory tubes leading from the spiracles to a body organ; it conducts respiratory gases to and from the tissues.

translocation: movement of soluble substances through the body.

triturate: to reduce in size mechanically; to crush or cut finely; to chew.

turbellarian: a flatworm; there are aquatic and terrestrial forms of these worms.

unicellular: an organism having but one cell.

urticarial: having the ability to cause itching.

ventral: referring to the belly or underside.

vertebrate: possessing a vertebral column or spine.

viviparous: the development of embryos within the

body of the (usually) female parent, whereby the developing young are nourished by the parent and are born as miniatures of the adult; rarely, fertilized ova are transferred to specialized structures in the male parent.

yolk: the fat and protein-rich reserves of eggs that provide the embryo with nutrients.

zygote: a very early embryonic stage that is formed on the union of sperm and egg.

Suggested Reading

Amos, W. H. (1967). **The Life of the Pond**. New York: McGraw-Hill Book Co., Inc.

Andrews, C. (1990). The Management of Aquatic Invertebrate Displays in Zoos. Pp. 21–27. *In*: **The Management and Welfare of Invertebrates in Captivity**. (N. M. Collins, Ed.). London: National Federation of Zoological Gardens of Great Britain and Ireland.

Andrews, M. (1977). **Life That Lives on Man**. New York: Taplinger.

Baerg, W. J. (1958). **The Tarantula**. Lawrence, KS: University of Kansas Press.

Barnes, R. D. (1974). **Invertebrate Zoology**. Philadelphia: W. B. Saunders Co.

Beklemshev, W. N. (1969). **Principles of Comparative Anatomy of Invertebrates**; (two volumes). Translated from the Russian by J. M. MacLennan; Z. Kabata, Editor. Edinburgh, England: Oliver and Boyd.

Biery, T. L. (1977). **Venomous Arthropod Handbook**. Washington, DC: Superintendent of Documents, U.S. Government Printing Office, Stock No. 008-070-00397-0.

Bodenheimer, F. S. (1951). **Insects as Human Food**. The Hague: The Netherlands; W. Junk.

Borror, D. and Delong, D. M. (1954). **Introduction to the Study of Insects**. New York: Holt, Rhinehart & Winston.

Bristowe, W. S. (1958). **The World of Spiders**. London: Collins.

Brues, C. T. (1946). **Insect Dietary: An Account of the Food Habits of Insects**. Cambridge: Harvard University Press.

Buchsbaum, R. (1948). **Animals Without Back-**

bones: An Introduction to Invertebrates. Chicago: Univ. Chicago Press.

Bulla, L. A. and Cheng, T. C., (Eds.). (1978) Invertebrate Models for Biomedical Research. New York: Plenum Press.

Byalynitskii-Birulya, A. A. (1965). Fauna of Russia and Adjacent Countries Vol. 1. Arachnoidea: Scorpions (N. V. Nasonov, Ed.). Translated from Russian by B. Munitz (E. Rabinowitz, Ed.). Jerusalem, Israel: S, Monson. Available from the Office of Technical Services, U.S. Department of Commerce, Washington, DC 20025. (Originally published in 1917).

Cantwell, G. E. (1974). Insect Diseases (two volumes). New York: Marcel Dekker.

Clarke, C. A. (1990). In Vitro Fertilization-Some Comparative Aspects. J. Royal Soc. Med., 83(4):214–218.

Cloudsley-Thompson, J. L. (1958). Spiders, Scorpions, Centipedes and Mites: The Ecology and Natural History of Woodlice, Myriapods and Arachnids. New York: Pergamon Press.

Collins, N. M. (Ed.). (1990). The Management and Welfare of Invertebrates in Captivity. London: National Federation of Zoological Gardens of Great Britain and Ireland.

——————(1990). Invertebrate Displays in the Zoos of the Future. Pp. 63–72. In: The Management and Welfare of Invertebrates in Captivity. (N. M. Collins, Ed.). London: National Federation of Zoological Gardens of Great Britain and Ireland.

Collins, L. M. and Hughes, D. G. (1990). Comments on the Management of Terrestrial Invertebrate Displays in Zoological Gardens. Pp. 29–32. In: The Management and Welfare of Invertebrates in Captivity. (N. M. Collins, Ed.). London: National Federation of Zoological Gardens of Great Britain and Ireland.

Comstock, J. H. (1940). An Introduction to Entomology. Ithaca, NY: Cornell University Press.

——————(1940). The Spider Book, Rev. Ed. W. J. Gertsch, (Ed.). New York: Doubleday, Doran and Co., Inc.

Cooper, E. K. (1961). Silkworms and Science—The Story of Silk. New York: Harcourt, Brace and World, Inc.

Cooper, J. E. (1976). Pets in Hospitals. *Brit. Med. J. 1*:698.

———(1980). Invertebrates and Invertebrate Diseases: An Introduction for the Veterinary Surgeon. *J. Small An. Pract., 21*:495–508.

———(1985). Invertebrates. Pp. 204–210. *In*: **Manual of Exotic Pets**. (J. E. Cooper & M. F. Hutchison, Eds.), Brit. Small Animal Veterinary Association. Cheltenham, England.

———(1987). A Veterinary Approach to Spiders. *J. Sm. An. Pract.* 28:229–239.

———(1990). Invertebrates—An Introduction. Pp. 7–14. *In*: **The Management and Welfare of Invertebrates in Captivity**. (N. M. Collins, Ed.). London: National Federation of Zoological Gardens of Great Britain and Ireland.

Cooper, M. E. (1990). Legal and Ethical Considerations in the Management and Welfare of Captive Invertebrates. Pp. 51–57. *In*: **The Management and Welfare of Invertebrates in Captivity**. (N. M. Collins, Ed.). London: National Federation of Zoological Gardens of Great Britain and Ireland.

Davidson, E. W. (Ed.). (1981). **Pathogenesis of Invertebrate Microbial Diseases** Totowa, NJ: Allanheld and Osmun & Co.

Denny, M. (1980). Locomotion: The Cost of Gastropod Crawling. *Science, 208*:1288–1290.

Department of Education and Sciences (England). (1971). Keeping Animals in Schools. Her Majesty's Stationery Office.

De Verde, M. A. and Machado-Allison, C. E. (1969). **Escorpiones**. Caracas, Venezuela: Caudernos Cientificos Direccion de Culture; Universidad Central de Venezuela.

Dougherty, E. C., Brown, Z. N., Hanson, E. D. and Hartman, W. D., (Eds.). (1963). **The Lower Metazoa; Comparative Biology and Physiology**. Berkeley, CA: University of California Press.

Ellis, S. (1978). **Invertebrate Rearer's Handbook**. Chelsea, England; Chelsea Printing Services.

Evans, H. E. (1933). Afield with the Spiders. Web Hunting in the Midlands and Woodlands and Along the Lanes. *Nat. Geogr, 64*(1):165–194.

Fabre, J.-H. (1923). **The Life of the Scorpion**. New York: Dodd, Mead & Co., Inc.

Farb, P. (Ed.). (1962). **The Insects**. New York: Time-Life Books.

Foelix, R. F. (1982). **Biology of Spiders**. Transl. with revisions from the German edition. Stuttgart, Fed. Rep. Germany. 1979. Cambridge: Harvard University Press.

Ford, E. B. (1955). **Moths**. New York: Macmillan.

———(1957). **Butterflies**. New York: Macmillan.

French, C. E., Licinsky, S. A., and Miller, D. R. (1957). Nutrient Composition of Earthworms. *J. Wildlife Mgmt.*, *21*:348.

Fretter, V. and Peake, J. (Eds.). (1975). **Pulmonates**, Vol. 1. Functional Anatomy. London: Academic Press.

———(1978). **Pulmonates**, Vol. 2A. Systematics, Evolution and Ecology. London: Academic Press.

Frost, S. W. (1959). **Insect Life and Insect Natural History**. New York: Dover Publications.

Frye, F. L. (1979). Diagnosis and Treatment of Some Common Diseases In *Uncommon* Pets. Pp. 76–91. *In*: Speakers' Syllabi, 91st Ann. Meeting and Scientific Seminar, California Veterinary Medical Assoc.

———(1986). Care and Feeding of Invertebrates Kept as Pets or Study Animals. Pp. 1039–1054. *In*: **Zoo & Wildlife Medicine**, 2nd Ed. (M. E. Fowler, Ed.). Philadelphia: W. B. Saunders.

———(1987). Praying Mantis: Friendly Denizen of the Garden. *Explorer, 29*(1):28–30.

———and Calvert, C. (1989). Preliminary Information on the Nutritional Content of Mulberry Silk Moth (*Bombyx mori*) **Larvae**. *J. Zoo and Wildlife Med.*, *20*(1):73–75.

———(1989). The Feeding of *Bombyx mori*, as Prey Insects for Captive Lizards: A Quantum Improvement over *Gryllus* spp., *Tenebrio molitor*, or *Galleria* spp. Section S4, First World Congress of Herpetology, Rutherford College, University of Kent, Canterbury, UK. 14 September, 1989.

Gaddie, R. E. and Gaddie, D. E. (1977). **Earthworms for Ecology & Profit**. in Two volumes. Ontario, CA: Bookworm Publishing Co.

Galtsoff, P. S. (1959). **Culture Methods for Invertebrate Animals**. American Assoc. for the Advancement of Science, New York: Dover Publications, Inc.

Gaul, A. (1953). **Wonderful World of Insects**. New York: Rhinehart.

Gertsch, W. J. and Newton, W. H. (1970). The Brown Recluse and the Black Widow Spiders. College Station, TX; Texas A & M University Fact Sheet No. L-623.

Gohl, B. (1975). Tropical Feeds. *FAO Agric. Ser.*, No 96. Rome: United Nations Food and Agriculture Organization.

Grange, J. M. and Davey, R. W. (1990). Antibacterial Properties of Propolis (Bee Glue). *J. Royal Soc. Med.*, 83:(3):159–160.

Harshbarger, J. C. (1973). Invertebrate Animals— What Can They Contribute to Cancer Research? *Fed. Proc.*, 32(12):2224–2226.

Hinshaw, S. H. and Sullivan, B. K. (1990). Predation on *Hyala versicolor* and *Pseudacris crucifer* During Reproduction. *J. Herpetol*, 24(2):196–197.

Holland, W. J. (1931). **Butterfly Book**. New York: Doubleday.

———(1949). **Moth Book**. New York: Doubleday.

Hölscher, U. (1985). **Vorkommen, Biologie und Toxicologie von Spinnen der Gattung *Latrodectus***. Dissertation Tierärztlichen Fakultät der Ludwig-Maximilians-Universität München.

Holt, V. M. (1988). **Why Not Eat Insects?**. London: Brit. Mus. Nat. His.; republished by E. W. Classey, Ltd.

Hunter, J. (1792). In Observations on Bees. *Phil. Trans. Royal Soc. London*, 27:186–188.

Imms, A.D. (1957). **General Textbook of Entomology**. New York: Dutton.

Iverson, E. S. and Skinner, R. H. (1977). **Land Hermit Crabs in Nature and as Pets**. Miami: Windward Publishing Co.

Keegan, H. L. (1980). **Scorpions of Medical Importance**. Jackson, MS: University of Mississippi.

Klass, P. (1989). **Vogelspinnen im Terrarium**. Stuttgart; Ulmer.

Klots, A. B. (1958). **World of Butterflies and Moths**. New York: McGraw-Hill.

Klots, A. B. and Klots, E. B. (1961). **Living Insects of the World**. New York: Doubleday.

Krishnaswami, S. Narasimhanna, S. M. N., Suryanarayan, S. K. and Kumararaj, S. S. (1973). **Manual** on Sericulture, V. 2. **Silkworm Rearing**. Rome: United Nations Food and Agriculture Organization.

Lapage, G. (1959). **Monig's Veterinary Helminthology and Entomology**, 4th Ed. Baltimore; Williams and Wilkins Co. 325–326.

Lawrence, R. D. and Millar, H. R. (1945). Protein Content of Earthworms. *Nature London, 155*:517.

Leung, W. W. (1968). **Food Composition Table for Use in Africa**. Rome: United Nations Food and Agriculture Organization.

————(1972). **Food Composition Table for Use in East Asia**. Rome: United Nations Food and Agriculture Organization.

Levi, H. W. and Levi, L. R. (1977). **A Guide to Spiders and their Kin**. New York: Golden Press.

Lim, B. L. (1966). Land Molluscs as Food of Malayan Rodents and Insectivores. *J. Zool. London, 148*:554–560.

Lutz, F. E. (1948). **Field Book of Insects**. New York: Putnam & Sons.

Mather, J. A. (1988). Ethical Treatment of Invertebrates: How Do We Define an Animal? Paper presented at the Animal Behavior Society Annual Meeting, Missoula, Montana.

Mead, A. R. (1979). **Pulmonates**, Vol. 2B; Economic Malacology with Particular Reference to *Achatina fulica*. V. Fretter and J. Peake, (Eds.). London: Academic Press.

Mesce, K. A. (1982). Calcium-Bearing Objects Elicit Shell Selection Behavior in a Hermit Crab. *Science* 215:993–995.

Miller, M. A. (1958). Earthworms and their Practical Value. Berkeley, CA: University of California Agricultural Extension Service Leafet Series.

Morel, G. (1978). Les Maladies Microbiennes des Arachnides (Arariens Exceptes). *Symp. Zoological Soc. London.* 42:477–481.

Morris, P. (1983). Annotated Outline of Captive Care of Snakes and Lizards. Special Publication No. 1. Davis, CA: Northern California Herpetological Society.

Murphy, F. (1980). **Keeping Spiders, Insects and Other Land Invertebrates in Captivity**. Edinburgh, Scotland: John Bartholomew & Sons.

Narasimhanna, S. M. N., Kasiuiswanathan, S. R. and Sastry, C. R. (1976). **Manual on Sericulture**, V.

1. **Mulberry Cultivation**. Rome: United Nations Food and Agriculture Organization.

National Federation of Zoological Gardens of Great Britain and Ireland (1990). **Codes of Practice for the Care of Invertebrates in Captivity: Euthanasia of Invertebrates**. Invertebrate Working Group, National Federation of Zoological Gardens, London.

Oldroyd, H. (1959). **Collection, Preserving and Studying Insects**. New York: Macmillan.

Passmore, L. (1933). California Trapdoor Spider Performs Engineering Marvels. *Nat. Geogr.* 64(1):195–211.

Payne, C. C. (1981). Cytoplasmic Polyhedrosis Viruses. Pp. 61–100. *In*: Davidson, E. W. (Ed.) **Pathogenesis of Invertebrate Microbial Diseases**. Totowa, New Jersey: Allanheld and Osmun & Co.

Peck, W. B. and Whitcomb, W. H. (1968). Feeding Spiders on Artificial Diet. *Entomological News* 79:233.

Perrero, L. and Perrero, L. (1979). **Tarantulas in Nature and As Pets**. Miami, FL: Windward Publishing Co.

Poinar, G. O. and Thomas, G. M. (1978). **Diagnostic Manual for the Identification of Insect Pathogens**. New York: Plenum Press.

Portmann, A. (1959). **Animal Camouflage**. Ann Arbor, MI: Univ. Michigan Press.

Prosser, C. L. (1973): Animal Models for Biomedical Research: V. Invertebrates. *Fed Proc.*, 32(12):2177–2230.

Ramsay, J. A. (1968). **Physiological Approaches to the Lower Animals**, 2nd Ed., London: Cambridge University Press.

Redford, K. H. and Dorea, J. G. (1984). The Nutritional Value of Invertebrates with Emphasis on Ants and Termites as Food for Mammals. *J. Zool. London*, 203:385–395.

Roeder, K. D. (1963). **Nerve Cells and Insect Behavior**. Cambridge: Harvard University Press.

Ross, E. S. (1953). **Insects Close Up**. Berkeley, CA: Univ. California Press.

Runham, N. W. and Hunter, P. J. (1970). **Terrestrial Slugs**. London: Hutchinson.

Runham, N. W., Isarankura, K. and Smith, B. J. (1965). Methods for Narcotizing and Anaesthetizing Gastropods. *Macalogica*, 2:231.

Sanderson, I. T. (1946). **Animal Tales: An An-**

thology of Animal Literature of All Countries. New York: Alfred A. Knopf.

Savory, T. H. (1961a). **Introduction to Arachnology**. London: Univ. London Press.

————(1961b). **Spiders, Men, and Scorpions: Being the History of Arachnology**. London: University of London Press.

————(1977). **Arachnids**, 2nd Ed. London: Academic Press.

Scheller, S., Stojko, A., Szwarniecka, I., Tustanowski, J., Obuszko, Z. (1977). Biological Properties of and Clinical Application of Propolis. 7. Investigation of the Influence of Ethanol Extract of Propolis (EEP) on Cartilaginous Tissue Regeneration. *Arzneimittelforschung*, 27:2138–2140.

Scheller, S., Ilewics, L., Luciak, M., Skrobidurska, D., and Matuga, W. (1878). Biological Properties and Clinical Application of Propolis. 9. Investigation of the Influence of Ethanol Extract of Propolis (EEP) on Dental Pulp Regeneration. *Arzneimittelforschung*, 28:289–291.

Schultz, S. A. (1984). The Tarantula Keeper's Guide. New York: Sterling Publishing.

Singh, P. (1977). Artificial Diets for Insects, Mites and Spiders. New York: Plenum Press.

Snow, K. R. (1970). **The Arachnids: An Introduction**. New York: Columbia University Press.

Softly, A. and Freeth, G. E. (1970). The Laboratory Maintenance of *Latrodectus mactans*. *J. Inst. Anim. Technicians* (U.K.), 21:117.

Sparks, A. K. (1972). **Invertebrate Pathology, Non-Communicable Diseases**. New York: Academic Press.

Stahnke, H. L. (1966). Some Aspects of Scorpion Behavior. *Bull. South. Calif. Acad. Sci.*, 65:65–80.

Stojko, A., Scheller, S., Szwarnowiecka, I., Tistanowski, J., Ostach, H., and Obuszko, Z. (1979). Biological Properties and Clinical Application of Propolis. 8. Experimental Observation on the Influence of Ethanol Extract of Propolis (EEP) on the Regeneration of Bone Tissue. *Arzneimittelforschung*, 28:35–37.

Storer, T. I. (1951). **General Zoology**, 2nd Ed. New York: McGraw-Hill Book Co.

Stowe, M. K., Tumlinson, J. H., and Heath, R. R. (1987). Chemical Mimicry: Bolas Spiders Emit Components of Moth Prey Species Sex Pheromones. *Science 236*:964–967.

Swain, R. B. (1952). **Insect Guide**. New York: Doubleday.

Taylor, R. L. (1975). **Butterflies in My Stomach**. Santa Barbara: Woodbridge Press Publ. Co.

UFAW (1976). **The UFAW Handbook on the Care and Management of Laboratory Animals**. Edinburgh, Scotland; Churchill Livingstone.

Ussinger, R. L. (Ed.). (1956). **Aquatic Insects of California With Keys to North American Genera and California Species**. Berkeley: Univ. California Press.

Wallach, J. D. (1979). The Management and Medical Care of Mealworms. *J. Zoo Anim. Med. 3*:29.

Weiser, J. (1977). **An Atlas of Insect Diseases**. The Hague, The Netherlands: W. Junk, Publishers.

Weygoldt, P. (1069). **The Biology of Pseudoscorpions**. Cambridge: Harvard University Press.

Wilmoth, J. H. (1967). **Biology of Invertebrates**. Englewood Cliffs, NJ: Prentice-Hall.

Wise, D. R. (1990). Management of Invertebrates for Animal Food. *In*: **The Management and Welfare of Invertebrates in Captivity**. (N. M. Collins, Ed.). London: National Federation of Zoological Gardens of Great Britain and Ireland.

Wu, Pang-chuan and Chen, Da-chuang (Transl. by Chen Zuo-pu, Liu, Ping-zhang, and Tang He) (1988). **Silkworm Rearing**. Rome: United Nations Food and Agriculture Organization Bulletin 73/2.

Zheng, Ting-zing, Tan, Yun-Fang, Huang, Guang-xing, Fan, Huaizhong, and Ma ben. (Transl. by Chen die-yun, Zhou, Qui-Hang ming, Hong-guang, and Chen Zue-pu) (1988). **Mulberry Cultivation**. Rome: United Nations Food and Agriculture Organization.

Index of Scientific Names Cited in Text

129

Species of Arachnids Currently Available in the Pet Trade Cross-referenced by Scientific Name

Androctonus sp.   Yellow "fat-tailed" scorpions*
Annandaliella pectinifera   Coimbatore brown tarantula*
Aphonopelma burica   Costa Rican blue-front tarantula
Aphonopelma heterops   Rio Grande gold tarantula
Aphonopelma seemanni   Costa Rican zebra tarantula
Avicularia avicularia   Pink-toed tarantula

Brachypelma (Eurypelma) albopilosa   Honduran curly-haired tarantula
Brachypelma (Eurypelma) chalcodes   Mexican blond tarantula
Brachypelma (Eurypelma) emilia   Mexican painted tarantula
Brachypelma (Eurypelma) smithi   Red-leg tarantula##
Buthotus sp.   Old world house scorpions*
Buthus occittanus   Old world yellow scorpion*

Ceratogyrus darlingi   African horned baboon spider*
Citharischius crawshayi   African giant baboon spider*

Dugesiella hentzi   Texas brown tarantula

Ephebopus murinus   Yellow flame-knee tarantula
Epibolus sp.   African millipedes
Eucratoscelus longiceps   Kenyan Voi red-rump baboon spider*

Grammostola actaeon   South American brown tarantula
Grammostola cala   Chilean red-backed tarantula
Grammostola iheringi   Argentine black tarantula
Grammostola spathulata   Chilean rose hair tarantula

Hadrurus sp.   Desert hairy scorpions
Hapalopus pentaloris   Costa Rican orange-banded tarantula
Haplopelma lividus   Burmese blue tarantula*

Harpactirella lightfooti	Bobbejaan baboon spider*
Heterometrus sp.	Asian black forest scorpions
Lasiodora klugi	Bahia scarlet "bird-eating" tarantula
Leiurus quinquestriatus	Yellow scorpion*
Megaphobema robusta	Giant Columbian bird-eating tarantula
Melopoeus albostmatus	Asian "bird-eating" tarantula
Melopoeus minax	Asian zebra tarantula
Metriopelma sp.	Costa Rican panther and tiger tarantulas
Opisthocanthus sp.	Yellow "creeping" scorpions
Opisthothalmus boehmi	Pale-legged scorpion
Palamnaeus fulviceps	Asian black scorpion
Pamphobeteus antinus	Bolivian steely blue tarantula
Pamphobeteus exsul	Rusty red "bird-eating" tarantula
Pamphobeteus wallacei	Peruvian striped tarantula
Pandinus imperator	African emperor scorpion
Phormictopus cancerides	Haitian tarantula
Poelcithothena regalis	Indian ornamental rainforest tarantula
Poelcithothena striata	Mysore rainforest tarantula
Pterinochilus vorax	Banded baboon spider*
Scolopendra heros	Texas orange centipede*
Scorpio mauris	Middle eastern gold scorpion*
Selenocosmia honesta	Fak Fak ochre tarantula*
Selenocosmia javanensis	Javanese yellow-kneed tarantula*
Selenocosmia lanipes	Mount Obrie tarantula*
Selenocosmia lyra	Banda Kwala tarantula*
Selenocosmia strubelli	Island chestnut tarantula*
Tarantula marginemaculata	Tailless whip scorpion
Theraphosa leblondi	Goliath "bird-eating" tarantula

legend: ##protected under International Convention; permits required for possession and/or transfer.
  *potentially serious venomous bites; not recommended for the novice.

General Subject Index

Notes

Notes

Notes

Notes

Notes